HOLT
1
SPANISH

¡Ven conmigo!®

Testing Program

HOLT, RINEHART AND WINSTON

A Harcourt Classroom Education Company

Austin · New York · Orlando · Atlanta · San Francisco · Boston · Dallas · Toronto · London

Contributing Writer:

Diane Donaho

Reviewers:

Richard Lindley

Mayanne Wright

Cover Photo/Illustration Credits:
Group of students: Marty Granger/HRW Photo

Photo Credits:
Page 200, Sam Dudgeon/HRW Photo; 329, Comstock

¡VEN CONMIGO! is a trademark licensed to Holt, Rinehart and Winston, registered in the United States of America and/or other jurisdictions.

Printed in the United States of America

ISBN 0-03-065537-4

1 2 3 4 5 6 7   066   05 04 03 02 01

Contents

Chapter Quizzes and Tests

Speaking Tests

To the Teacher

The ¡Ven conmigo! Testing Program contains the following assessment materials: quizzes, Chapter Tests, and Speaking Tests. For other assessment options, such as performance assessment or portfolio suggestions, see the Alternative Assessment Guide. The Testing Program is organized by chapter, and each chapter contains these components:

- **Quizzes** Six quizzes accompany each chapter, two quizzes for each **paso**. Each is short enough to be administered within approximately 20 minutes, leaving ample time for other activities. The first quiz for each **paso** (Quiz A) focuses on the grammar and vocabulary for that section of the chapter. These Grammar and Vocabulary quizzes principally test writing and reading skills, and feature more discrete-point, closed-ended assessment. They may be used for evaluation, or as review in preparation for the second quiz in each **paso** and the Chapter Tests. The **paso** quizzes (Quiz B) assess listening, reading, and writing skills as well as culture, using a combination of closed and open-ended formats. Listening and reading sections evaluate comprehension of the **paso** material, while the writing portion asks students to express themselves in real-life situations. You will find the listening section of each **paso** quiz (Quiz B) recorded on the Audio Compact Discs for the corresponding chapter. The scripts and answers to all the quizzes are also included in the Testing Program. For ease in grading, the total point value for three quizzes, one from each **paso**, equals 100. The Grammar and Vocabulary quiz for each **paso** (Quiz A) always has the same point value as its Quiz B counterpart, allowing you to choose to administer either of the two quizzes in any given **paso**. Alternative grammar and vocabulary quizzes for each **paso** can be found in the Student Make-Up Assignments with Alternative Quizzes.

- **Chapter Tests** The Chapter Tests for Chapters 1–12 include listening, reading, writing, and culture segments. They are designed to be completed in one class period. Score sheets are provided with the tests, as well as listening scripts and answer keys. With the exception of the writing and some culture segments, the Chapter Tests are designed to facilitate mechanical or electronic scoring. You will find the listening segments for the Chapter Tests recorded on the Audio Compact Discs.

- **Midterm and Final Exams** The Midterm Exam is a comprehensive exam covering material from Chapters 1–6, while the Final Exam focuses on material from Chapters 7–12. These exams evaluate listening, reading, writing, and culture. As in the Chapter Tests, the listening, reading, and some of the culture sections are designed to facilitate mechanical or electronic scoring. Score sheets, scripts, and answers are provided for both exams. You will find the listening portions of these exams on Audio Compact Discs 6 and 12 respectively.

- **Speaking Tests** There is one Speaking Test for each chapter. For more detailed suggestions on administering and grading these tests, see "To the Teacher" and the rubrics on pages 341 and 342 of this book.

Nombre _____ Clase _____ Fecha _____

¡Mucho gusto!

Quiz 1-1A

PRIMER PASO

Maximum Score: 35

Grammar and Vocabulary

A. Match each question or statement in the column on the left with the most appropriate response from the right-hand column. (10 points)

_____ 1. ¡Buenos días, don Raimundo!

_____ 2. ¿Cómo estás hoy?

_____ 3. Adiós, señora Huerta.

_____ 4. ¿Cómo te llamas?

_____ 5. Encantado.

a. Hasta mañana, Miguel.
b. Hola, Margarita.
c. Igualmente.
d. Estoy bien, gracias.
e. Me llamo Carmen.

SCORE _____

B. Complete the conversation between Carmen and Juan Felipe with the expressions from the box. (9 points)

| Tengo que irme | Más o menos | me llamo | Encantada | Estupenda |
| qué tal | | Igualmente | Hasta luego | estás |

CARMEN ¡Hola! ¿Cómo te llamas?

JUAN FELIPE Hola, _____ 6. Juan Felipe Barreras. ¿Y tú?

CARMEN Soy Carmen Hurtado. _____ 7. .

JUAN FELIPE _____ 8. . ¿Cómo _____ 9. hoy, Carmen?

CARMEN _____ 10. , gracias. Y tú, ¿_____ 11. ?

JUAN FELIPE _____ 12. . Tengo clase ahora. _____ 13. .

CARMEN Bueno, Juan Felipe. _____ 14. .

SCORE _____

Quiz 1-1A

C. Nine of the items on Ben's spelling quiz are missing accents, tildes, or punctuation marks. Write the correct form of each word or expression below. (9 points)

15. Adios. _____

16. senora _____

17. Buenos dias. _____

18. Qué tal? _____

19. ¿Como te llamas? _____

20. Mucho gusto! _____

21. ¿Y tu? _____

22. manana _____

23. Este es mi amigo. _____

SCORE [   ]

D. Indicate the subject of each statement or question by writing **yo** or **tú** next to each. (7 points)

_____ 24. Me llamo Pilar.

_____ 25. Bueno, tengo clase.

_____ 26. ¿Cómo te llamas?

_____ 27. Estoy estupenda, gracias.

_____ 28. ¿Cómo estás hoy?

_____ 29. Tengo que irme.

_____ 30. ¿Te llamas Laura?

SCORE [   ]

TOTAL SCORE [/35]

Nombre _____ Clase _____ Fecha _____

1 ¡Mucho gusto!

Quiz 1-1B

■ PRIMER PASO

Maximum Score: 35

I. Listening

A. Listen to some people saying hello, introducing friends, or saying goodbye. Put a check mark in the appropriate column. (10 points)

	Greeting	Introduction	Goodbye
1.			
2.			
3.			
4.			
5.			

SCORE _____

II. Reading

B. Read the conversation between three students, then indicate if the statements that follow are **a) cierto** (*true*) or **b) falso** (*false*). (10 points)

TERESA   Buenas tardes, Juan. ¿Cómo estás?
JUAN   Bien, gracias. ¿Y tú?
TERESA   Estoy regular, gracias. Juan, ésta es mi amiga Maribel.
JUAN   Encantado, Maribel.
MARIBEL   Mucho gusto, Juan.

_____ **6.** This conversation takes place in the morning.

_____ **7.** Teresa and Juan don't know each other.

_____ **8.** Teresa is feeling okay today.

_____ **9.** Maribel and Teresa are friends.

_____ **10.** Maribel and Juan are meeting for the first time.

SCORE _____

Quiz 1-1 B

III. Writing

C. Martín and Clara meet for the first time. Complete their conversation by filling in the blank with the appropriate word(s). (10 points)

11. MARTÍN   _____ días. _____ Martín. ¿Y

                _____? ¿_____ te llamas?

12. CLARA   Me _____ Clara.

13. MARTÍN   Mucho _____.

14. CLARA   _____.

15. MARTÍN   Bueno, tengo que _____. _____ mañana.

16. CLARA   _____.

SCORE [   ]

IV. Culture

D. Read each of the following statements. Based on the information in your textbook, indicate if the statement is **a) cierto** (*true*) or **b) falso** (*false*). (5 points)

_____ 17. If María Isabel's last name is Chávez García, her mother's maiden name is Chávez.

_____ 18. Spanish speakers commonly greet each other with a warm hug or light kiss on the cheek.

_____ 19. Many people in the Spanish-speaking world celebrate not only their birthdays, but also the feast day of the saint they are named after.

_____ 20. The name Arnoldo Pérez Pino would be listed under Pino in the phone book.

_____ 21. People in Spanish-speaking countries usually sit closer to each other than people in the United States.

SCORE [   ]

TOTAL SCORE [/35]

¡Mucho gusto!

Quiz 1-2A

SEGUNDO PASO

Maximum Score: 30

Grammar and Vocabulary

A. Leticia is telling you the phone numbers of some classmates. Write out the phone numbers in numerals. (5 points)

1. El número de Nuria es el dos tres cinco, once veintiséis. _____

2. El número de Pedro es el siete nueve uno, trece catorce. _____

3. El número de Lucho es el ocho cuatro seis, quince veintisiete. _____

4. El número de Marta es el tres seis siete, doce dieciséis. _____

5. El número de Jesús es el cuatro cinco nueve, veinticuatro treinta. _____

SCORE _____

B. Solve these math problems and write them out, spelling all numbers as words. (10 points)

6. _____ + _____ = _____
         20   5

7. _____ + _____ = _____
         12   1

8. _____ + _____ = _____
          4   11

9. _____ + _____ = _____
         22   8

10. _____ + _____ = _____
          14   2

SCORE _____

Quiz 1-2A

CAPÍTULO 1

C. Ask and explain where new classmates are from, using the correct form of the verb **ser.** (10 points)

11. Yo _____ de Chicago.

12. Luisa _____ de Miami.

13. Rafael _____ de México.

14. ¿Tú _____ de California?

15. Mi amiga Alicia _____ de San Antonio.

SCORE [   ]

D. Complete everyone's questions with the correct question words. (5 points)

16. Hola, Luis, ¿_____ tal?

17. Hola, Beni, ¿_____ estás?

18. Carla, ¿de _____ eres?

19. Hola, soy Lupe. ¿_____ te llamas?

20. Beto, ¿_____ años tienes?

SCORE [   ]

TOTAL SCORE [   ] /30

Spanish 1 ¡Ven conmigo!, Chapter 1

CAPÍTULO 1

¡Mucho gusto!

■ SEGUNDO PASO

I. Listening

A. Some new friends are asking and telling ages. Write each person's age in the blank. Use numerals. (10 points)

1. _____

2. _____

3. _____

4. _____

5. _____

SCORE _____

II. Reading

B. You received this note from one of your new classmates at the Spanish high school you're attending. Read the note and then complete the statements that follow in English. (8 points)

> ¡Hola! ¿Cómo te llamas? Me llamo Miguel. ¿Qué tal? Yo, muy bien. ¿De dónde eres? ¿Cuántos años tienes? ¡Hasta luego!

Miguel wants to know . . .

6. _____

7. _____

8. _____

9. _____

SCORE _____

Quiz 1-2B

III. Writing

C. You're interviewing a new student at your high school. Write two possible questions and two possible answers. (8 points)

10. _____

_____

11. _____

_____

12. _____

_____

13. _____

_____

SCORE [   ]

D. Solve the following math problems. Write your answers in Spanish as words, not numerals. (4 points)

14. cuatro + ocho = _____

15. treinta − siete = _____

16. trece + siete = _____

17. catorce + dos = _____

SCORE [   ]

TOTAL SCORE [   ] /30

Spanish 1 ¡Ven conmigo!, Chapter 1

Nombre _____ Clase _____ Fecha _____

¡Mucho gusto!

TERCER PASO

Quiz 1-3A

Maximum Score: 35

Grammar and Vocabulary

A. Complete the lists below with the Spanish words that belong in each category. Include definite articles in your answers. (15 points)

deportes

1. _____
2. _____
3. _____
4. _____

tipos de *(types of)* música

7. _____
8. _____

comida

5. _____
6. _____

clases

9. _____
10. _____

SCORE [   ]

B. Ana and Luis are talking about sports. Complete their conversation with the missing words from the box. (12 points)

gusta	no	te	más
Qué	mucho	me	pero

LUIS   Ana, ¿_____ gusta el fútbol?
                      11.

ANA   Sí, _____ gusta, _____ me gusta más el tenis.
                      12.   **13.**

LUIS   ¡Uf! El tenis _____ me gusta. ¡Es horrible!
                      14.

ANA   ¿_____ te gusta?
              15.

LUIS   Pues, me gusta _____ el baloncesto.
                              16.

ANA   ¿Y la natación?

LUIS   Sí, me _____ , pero me gusta _____ el baloncesto.
                      17.   **18.**

SCORE [   ]

Spanish 1 ¡Ven conmigo!, Chapter 1

Testing Program **9**

CAPITULO 1

 Quiz 1-3A

C. You are talking with Marcos, the new student. In Spanish, ask Marcos if he likes . . . (8 points)

19. English class _____

_____

20. the cafeteria _____

_____

Now explain to Marcos that . . .

21. you don't like homework. _____

_____

22. you like Chinese food, but you like Mexican food more. _____

_____

SCORE [＿＿＿＿]

TOTAL SCORE [＿＿＿＿ /35]

Nombre _____ Clase _____ Fecha _____

¡Mucho gusto!

Maximum Score: 35

■ TERCER PASO

I. Listening

A. Look at the pictures and listen to students saying what they like or don't like. If the sentence agrees with the illustration, write **sí**. If not, write **no**. (8 points)

1. _____

2. _____

3. _____

4. _____

SCORE _____

II. Reading

B. Read the following dialogue. Then read the statements on page 12. Based on the information in your textbook, indicate if each statement is **cierto** (*true*) or **falso** (*false*). (16 points)

TOMÁS	Hola, Luisa. ¿Qué tal? ¿Bien?
LUISA	Sí, muy bien, gracias. Y tú, ¿cómo estás?
TOMÁS	Regular, más o menos.
LUISA	Ésta es mi amiga, Marisol.
TOMÁS	Mucho gusto.
MARISOL	Encantada, Tomás.
TOMÁS	Marisol, ¿de dónde eres?
MARISOL	Soy de Segovia, España. Y tú, ¿de dónde eres?
TOMÁS	Yo soy de los Estados Unidos.
MARISOL	¿Cuántos años tienes?
TOMÁS	Tengo quince años. ¿Y tú?
MARISOL	Dieciséis. ¿Te gusta la comida china?
TOMÁS	No, pero me gusta la comida mexicana.
LUISA	A mí me gusta la comida mexicana, pero me gusta más la comida italiana.
MARISOL	A mí también me gusta la comida italiana.
TOMÁS	Entonces, vamos (*let's go*) al restaurante italiano.

Spanish 1 ¡Ven conmigo!, Chapter 1

Quiz 1-3B

_____ 5. Luisa is not feeling very well today.

_____ 6. Tomás and Marisol are from the same country.

_____ 7. Tomás is 15 years old.

_____ 8. Marisol is 17 years old.

_____ 9. Tomás and Marisol know each other very well.

_____ 10. Tomás does not like Chinese food.

_____ 11. Tomás and Luisa both like Mexican food.

_____ 12. Luisa likes Italian food more than Mexican food.

SCORE ☐

III. Writing

C. Using the cues in parentheses, complete each sentence below by filling in the blanks. Be sure to use **el** or **la** in your answer. (5 points)

13. Me gusta _____. (name a sport)

14. ¿Te gusta _____? (name a type of music)

15. No me gusta _____. (name one type of food)

16. Pero me gusta _____. (name another type of food)

17. Me gusta más _____. (name a class)

SCORE ☐

D. Answer the following questions with a sentence that has at least five words. (6 points)

18. ¿Te gusta más el inglés o *(or)* el español?

_____

19. ¿Te gusta la música clásica? _____

20. ¿Qué te gusta más, la música de Brandy o la música de No Doubt?

_____

SCORE ☐

TOTAL SCORE ☐ /35

CUMULATIVE SCORE FOR QUIZZES 1–3 ☐ /100

¡Mucho gusto!

Chapter 1 Test

I. Listening

Maximum Score: 30 points

A. Write the letter of the illustration that best matches the situation you hear. (15 points)

a.

b.

c.

d.

e.

1. _____

2. _____

3. _____

4. _____

5. _____

SCORE [ ]

B. Several friends are greeting each other and introducing new students. Choose the best answer to the question that you hear from the choices below. (15 points)

_____ **6. a.** Te llamas Antonio.
   b. Hasta luego.
   c. Me llamo Pepe.

_____ **7. a.** Soy de España.
   b. Tengo 16 años.
   c. Eres de México.

_____ **8. a.** Tengo 14 años.
   b. Tienes 16 años.
   c. Soy de México.

Chapter 1 Test

_____ **9. a.** Ésta es mi amiga Patricia.
      b. Me gusta el béisbol.
      c. Yo soy Beatriz.

_____ **10. a.** No, no me gusta el baloncesto.
       b. Sí, me gusta el fútbol.
       c. Sí, me llamo Luis.

SCORE [   ]

II. Reading

Maximum Score: 30 points

Carlos and Rolando are pen pals who live in Spain. Read the postcards that they have written to one another and then answer the questions.

Hola, Rolando, ¿cómo estás? Yo estoy muy bien. Me llamo Carlos y soy de Sevilla. Tengo quince años y me gustan el tenis, la comida china y la música rock. ¿Cuántos años tienes? ¿Qué te gusta? ¡Hasta luego!

Tu amigo,
Carlos

Hola Carlos,
Me llamo Rolando y soy de Madrid. Yo también tengo quince años. Me gusta el béisbol, pero no me gusta el tenis. A mí me gustan más la comida china y la música clásica, pero no me gusta la comida italiana. ¡Hasta luego!
Escríbeme pronto,
Rolando

C. Who would most likely have made the following statements, **a)** Carlos, **b)** Rolando, or **c)** both? (15 points)

_____ 11. Tengo quince años.

_____ 12. Me gusta la comida china.

_____ 13. Me gusta el béisbol.

_____ 14. Soy de Sevilla.

_____ 15. No me gusta el tenis.

D. Indicate whether the following statements are **a) cierto** *(true)* or **b) falso** *(false)*. (15 points)

_____ 16. Rolando is from the United States.

_____ 17. Carlos is 14 years old.

_____ 18. Carlos likes Chinese food.

_____ 19. Rolando likes Italian food and Chinese food.

_____ 20. Carlos is from Madrid.

SCORE [ ]

III. Culture

Maximum Score: 10 points

E. Based on the information from your textbook, indicate whether the following statements are **a) cierto** *(true)* or **b) falso** *(false)*. (6 points)

_____ 21. Most people in Spanish-speaking countries have two last names, first the father's last name and then the mother's maiden name.

_____ 22. If you are in a new country, a good way to behave politely is to watch others and follow their lead.

SCORE [ ]

Chapter 1 Test

F. Alphabetize the names in the box as they would appear in the phone book in a Spanish-speaking country. (4 points)

> María Graciela Pérez Ávila   Rolando Martín Fierro Guerrero
>
> Marco Arnoldo Soto Garza   Orieta Alicia Ramírez García

23. _____

24. _____

25. _____

26. _____

SCORE ☐

IV. Writing

Maximum Score: 30 points

G. Answer the following questions about yourself in complete sentences in Spanish. (10 points)

27. ¿Cómo te llamas?

_____

28. ¿Cómo estás?

_____

29. ¿De dónde eres?

_____

30. ¿Qué deporte te gusta?

_____

31. ¿Cuántos años tienes?

_____

SCORE ☐

Nombre _____ Clase _____ Fecha _____

H. Create five questions or statements that you would include in a conversation with a new student. Combine one word or phrase from each box. Not all words will be used. (10 points)

¿Cuántos Me	de catorce
¿Cómo Soy	gusta estás
¿De dónde Tengo	eres años

el fútbol.
Michigan.   años.
tú?   tienes?

32. _____

_____

33. _____

_____

34. _____

_____

35. _____

_____

36. _____

_____

SCORE _____

CAPÍTULO 1

Chapter 1 Test

I. Write a sentence in Spanish for each picture saying whether you like or don't like what is shown. Be sure to use the correct definite article (**el** or **la**) in each sentence. (10 points)

37. _____

_____

38. _____

_____

39. _____

_____

40. _____

_____

41. _____

_____

SCORE ☐

TOTAL SCORE ☐ /100

Spanish 1 ¡Ven conmigo!, Chapter 1

Nombre _____ Clase _____ Fecha _____

Circle the letter that matches the most appropriate response.

I. Listening
Maximum Score: 30 points

A. (15 points)

1. a b c d e
2. a b c d e
3. a b c d e
4. a b c d e
5. a b c d e

SCORE [   ]

B. (15 points)

6. a b c
7. a b c
8. a b c
9. a b c
10. a b c

SCORE [   ]

II. Reading
Maximum Score: 30 points

C. (15 points)

11. a b c
12. a b c
13. a b c
14. a b c
15. a b c

SCORE [   ]

D. (15 points)

16. a b
17. a b
18. a b
19. a b
20. a b

SCORE [   ]

III. Culture
Maximum Score: 10 points

E. (6 points)

21. a b
22. a b

SCORE [   ]

F. (4 points)

23. _____
24. _____
25. _____
26. _____

SCORE [   ]

IV. Writing Maximum Score: 30 points

G. (10 points)

27. _____
28. _____
29. _____
30. _____
31. _____

SCORE ▭

H. (10 points)

32. _____
_____
33. _____
_____
34. _____
_____
35. _____
_____
36. _____
_____

SCORE ▭

I. (10 points)

37. _____
38. _____
39. _____
40. _____
41. _____

SCORE ▭

TOTAL SCORE ▭ /100

Spanish 1 ¡Ven conmigo!, Chapter 1

Quiz 1-1 B Capítulo 1 Primer paso

I. Listening

A. 1. — Buenas tardes, María. ¿Qué tal?
    2. — Adiós, Luisa, hasta mañana.
    3. — Hola, Juan. ¿Cómo estás?
    4. — Yo soy María. Y tú, ¿cómo te llamas?
       — Me llamo Margarita. Mucho gusto.
    5. — Marcos, éste es Rafael.
       — Encantado.
       — Igualmente.

Quiz 1-2B Capítulo 1 Segundo paso

I. Listening

A. 1. — Tengo trece años.
    2. — ¿Cuántos años tienes?
       — Tengo veintiséis años.
    3. — Tengo quince años.
    4. — Tú tienes treinta años, ¿verdad?
       — Sí, treinta.
    5. — Tengo veintiún años.

Quiz 1-3B Capítulo 1 Tercer paso

I. Listening

A. 1. A mí me gusta más el fútbol.
    2. Me gusta la clase de español.
    3. No me gusta el tenis, pero me gusta el baloncesto.
    4. ¿Qué te gusta? ¿La comida china?

CAPÍTULO 1

ANSWERS Quiz 1-1A

A. (10 points: 2 points per item)
1. b
2. d
3. a
4. e
5. c

B. (9 points: 1 point per item)
6. me llamo
7. Encantada
8. Igualmente
9. estás
10. Estupenda
11. qué tal
12. Más o menos
13. Tengo que irme
14. Hasta luego

C. (9 points: 1 point per item)
15. Adiós.
16. señora
17. Buenos días.
18. ¿Qué tal?
19. ¿Cómo te llamas?
20. ¡Mucho gusto!
21. ¿Y tú?
22. mañana
23. Éste es mi amigo.

D. (7 points: 1 point per item)
24. yo
25. yo
26. tú
27. yo
28. tú
29. yo
30. tú

ANSWERS Quiz 1-1B

I. Listening

A. (10 points: 2 points per item)

	Greeting	Introduction	Goodbye
1.	✓		
2.			✓
3.	✓		
4.		✓	
5.		✓	

II. Reading

B. (10 points: 2 points per item)
6. b
7. b
8. a
9. a
10. a

III. Writing

C. (10 points: 1 point per item)
11. Buenos, Soy/Me llamo, tú, Cómo
12. llamo
13. gusto
14. Igualmente/Encantada
15. irme, Hasta
16. Adiós/Chao/Hasta luego

IV. Culture

D. (5 points: 1 point per item)
17. b
18. a
19. a
20. b
21. a

ANSWERS Quiz 1-2A

A. (5 points: 1 point per item)
1. 235-1126
2. 791-1314
3. 846-1527
4. 367-1216
5. 459-2430

B. (10 points: 2 points per item)
6. veinte + cinco = veinticinco
7. doce + uno = trece
8. cuatro + once = quince
9. veintidós + ocho = treinta
10. catorce + dos = dieciséis

C. (10 points: 2 points per item)
11. soy
12. es
13. es
14. eres
15. es

D. (5 points: 1 point per item)
16. qué
17. cómo
18. dónde
19. Cómo
20. cuántos

ANSWERS Quiz 1-2B

I. Listening

A. (10 points: 2 points per item)
1. 13
2. 26
3. 15
4. 30
5. 21

II. Reading

B. (8 points: 2 points per item)
6. what my name is
7. how I'm doing
8. where I'm from
9. how old I am

III. Writing

C. (8 points: 2 points per item)
Answers will vary. Possible answers:
10. ¿Cómo te llamas?
11. Me llamo Juan.
12. ¿De dónde eres?
13. Soy de Chile.

D. (4 points: 1 point per item)
14. doce
15. veintitrés
16. veinte
17. dieciséis

CAPÍTULO 1

ANSWERS Quiz 1-3A

A. (15 points, 1.5 points per item)
Some answers may vary.
Possible answers:
1. el baloncesto
2. el fútbol
3. el tenis
4. la natación
5. la ensalada
6. la fruta
7. el jazz
8. la música rock
9. el español
10. el inglés

B. (12 points: 1.5 points per item)
11. te
12. me
13. pero
14. no
15. Qué
16. mucho
17. gusta
18. más

C. (8 points: 2 points per item)
19. ¿Te gusta la clase de inglés?
20. ¿Te gusta la cafetería?
21. No me gusta la tarea.
22. Me gusta la comida china, pero me gusta más la comida mexicana.

ANSWERS Quiz 1-3B

I. Listening

A. (8 points: 2 points per item)
1. sí
2. sí
3. sí
4. no

II. Reading

B. (16 points: 2 points per item)
5. falso
6. falso
7. cierto
8. falso
9. falso
10. cierto
11. cierto
12. cierto

III. Writing

C. (5 points: 1 point per item)
Answers will vary. Possible answers:
13. el tenis
14. la música pop
15. la comida mexicana
16. la comida china
17. el español

D. (6 points: 2 points per item)
Answers will vary. Possible answers:
18. Me gusta más el inglés.
19. Sí, me gusta la música clásica.
20. Me gusta más la música de Brandy.

Scripts *for* Chapter 1 Test

I. Listening

A. 1. — ¿Cuántos años tienes?
        — Tengo diecisiete.
    2. — Soy de los Estados Unidos.
    3. — Buenos días, señora Chávez.
    4. — Mucho gusto.
        — Encantado.
    5. — ¿Qué te gusta? ¿El baloncesto?

B. 6. — ¿Cómo te llamas?
    7. — ¿De dónde eres?
    8. — ¿Cuántos años tienes?
    9. — Yo soy Patricia. ¿Y tú?
   10. — ¿Qué te gusta? ¿El baloncesto?

Answers to Chapter 1 Test

I. Listening Maximum Score: 30 points

A. (15 points: 3 points per item)
1. d
2. b
3. c
4. a
5. e

B. (15 points: 3 points per item)
6. c
7. a
8. a
9. c
10. a

II. Reading Maximum Score: 30 points

C. (15 points: 3 points per item)
11. c
12. c
13. b
14. a
15. b

D. (15 points: 3 points per item)
16. b
17. b
18. a
19. b
20. b

III. Culture Maximum Score: 10 points

E. (6 points: 3 points per item)
21. a
22. a

F. (4 points: 1 point per item)
23. Rolando Martín Fierro Guerrero
24. María Graciela Pérez Ávila
25. Orieta Alicia Ramírez García
26. Marco Arnoldo Soto Garza

IV. Writing Maximum Score: 30 points

G. (10 points: 2 points per item)
Answers will vary. Possible answers:
27. Me llamo (*student's name*).
28. Estoy bien.
29. Soy de los Estados Unidos.
30. Me gusta la natación.
31. Tengo (*student's age*) años.

H. (10 points: 2 points per item)
Answers should include five of the following:
32. Soy de Michigan.
33. Tengo catorce años.
34. ¿Cómo estás tú?
35. Me gusta el fútbol.
36. ¿De dónde eres?
   ¿Cuántos años tienes?

I. (10 points: 2 points per item)
Answers will vary. Possible answers:
37. (No) me gusta el fútbol norteamericano.
38. (No) me gusta la música.
39. (No) me gusta el tenis.
40. (No) me gusta el fútbol.
41. (No) me gusta la comida italiana.

CAPÍTULO 2

¡Organízate!

■ PRIMER PASO

Grammar and Vocabulary

A. Your friend wants to learn some Spanish. Tell him the Spanish words for the things he needs to . . . (7 points)

1. draw a straight line _____

2. multiply and divide _____

3. carry books and school supplies _____

4. find out how to spell a word _____

5. write in ink _____

6. hold loose papers _____

7. write an essay or do his homework on _____

SCORE _____

B. What does everyone need to buy? Complete the sentences with the correct indefinite article. (8 points)

8. Necesito _____ calculadora y _____ cuaderno.

9. ¿Necesitas _____ mochila o _____ carpeta?

10. Mi amigo necesita _____ goma de borrar y _____ lápiz.

11. Laura necesita _____ diccionario y _____ regla.

SCORE _____

Nombre _____ Clase _____ Fecha _____

Quiz 2-1A

C. You found several of each of the things below when cleaning out your backpack and desk. Write the plural form of each noun with its correct indefinite article. (12 points)

12. papel _____

13. goma _____

14. libro _____

15. lápiz _____

16. cuaderno _____

17. carpeta _____

SCORE [ ]

D. Complete these statements about what different people need and want to buy at the bookstore with the correct subject pronoun: **yo**, **tú**, **él**, or **ella**. (8 points)

18. _____ necesito un diccionario para la clase de español.

19. ¿Y Pedro? ¿Qué necesita _____ ?

20. Luisa, ¿_____ necesitas papel?

21. ¿Qué necesita la profesora? _____ necesita más libros.

22. _____ quiero muchas cosas.

23. ¿Qué quiere tu amiga Mariana? ¿_____ quiere una mochila?

24. ¿Y el señor Ponce? _____ quiere una calculadora.

25. ¿_____ quieres un diccionario en español o un diccionario en inglés?

SCORE [ ]

TOTAL SCORE [/35]

Spanish 1 ¡Ven conmigo!, Chapter 2

Nombre _____ Clase _____ Fecha _____

CAPÍTULO

2 ¡Organízate!

Quiz 2-1B

Maximum Score: 35

■ PRIMER PASO

I. Listening

A. Listen as Clara talks about what she has or doesn't have in her backpack. Look at the drawings and decide, based on what you hear, if the items are in the backpack or not. Circle **sí** or **no** for each item below. (10 points)

1. sí   no

4. sí   no

2. sí   no

5. sí   no

3. sí   no

SCORE [____]

II. Reading

B. Read the advertisements for **Papelería Ferrer** and **Casa del Libro**. Then answer the questions that follow in English. (10 points)

Papelería Ferrer Fundada en 1856 bolígrafos — cuadernos lápices — calculadoras carpetas — reglas papel para cartas C/ Juan Bravo, 98 Madrid 28010 ☎ 263 31 55

Casa del Libro Gran oferta para la vuelta al colegio La mejor selección de libros de texto Cuadernos y papel Diccionarios Español, Español-Inglés Libros Mochilas C/ Princesa, 33 Madrid 28006 ☎ 442 47 77

CAPÍTULO 2

Spanish 1 ¡Ven conmigo!, Chapter 2

Testing Program **29**

Quiz 2-1B

6. If you needed a backpack, which store would you go to? _____

7. If you needed some folders, which store would you choose? _____

8. What item(s) do both stores mention in their advertisements? _____

9. Which store specializes in textbooks? _____

10. You need some things for your math class. Which store would you go to, and what would you buy? _____

SCORE [   ]

III. Writing

C. Write five sentences, explaining what Paco and Mercedes need for school. Use subject pronouns and pay attention to whether each item is singular or plural. (10 points)

Paco   11. _____

Paco   12. _____

Paco   13. _____

Mercedes   14. _____

Mercedes   15. _____

SCORE [   ]

IV. Culture

D. Read each of the following statements. Based on what you've learned in your textbook, write a) **cierto** or b) **falso** in each blank. (5 points)

_____ 16. In many high schools in Spanish-speaking countries, teachers change classrooms while students stay in the same classroom all day.

_____ 17. Lockers are commonplace in schools throughout Spain and Latin America.

SCORE [   ]

TOTAL SCORE [   ] /35

CAPÍTULO 2

CAPÍTULO 2

¡Organízate!

Quiz 2-2A

■ SEGUNDO PASO

Maximum Score: 35

Grammar and Vocabulary

A. Complete Fernando's description of his room with the missing Spanish equivalents of the English words in parentheses. (9 points)

¿Cómo es mi _____ ? Pues, tengo _____ y
　　　　　　　1. (*room*)　　　　　　　　　　　**2.** (*a bed*)

_____ . También tengo _____ y _____ . Y
　3. (*a closet*)　　　　　　　　　**4.** (*a chair*)　　　　**5.** (*a lamp*)

hay dos _____ y _____ . Tengo _____ y
　　　　6. (*windows*)　　　　　**7.** (*a door*)　　　　　**8.** (*a radio*)

_____ también.
9. (*some posters*)

SCORE ☐

B. Explain how many of each item are left in the department store after the sale. Use **hay** and the inventory chart below. Write all numbers as words. (12 points)

armarios	18
relojes	25
camas	21
escritorios	12
mesas	15
televisores	30

10. _____

11. _____

11. _____

13. _____

14. _____

15. _____

SCORE ☐

CAPÍTULO 2

Quiz 2-2A

C. Complete the questions and statements about what people have and need with the correct forms of **cuánto** and **mucho**. Remember to make these adjectives match the nouns they describe. (14 points)

16. ¿_____ revistas quieres?

17. Hay _____ libros en la clase.

18. ¿_____ sillas hay en la cafetería?

19. ¿Tienes _____ carteles en tu cuarto?

20. Necesito _____ ropa para el colegio.

21. ¿_____ papeles tienes en tu mochila?

22. No tengo _____ lámparas en mi cuarto.

SCORE _____

TOTAL SCORE _____ /35

Spanish 1 ¡Ven conmigo!, Chapter 2

CAPÍTULO 2

2 ¡Organízate!

■ SEGUNDO PASO

I. Listening

A. Listen as some friends ask each other questions. Match each friend's name with the picture of the items he or she has. (6 points)

_____ 1. Luisa

_____ 2. Pedro

_____ 3. Alicia

_____ 4. Carlos

_____ 5. Ana

_____ 6. Juan

a.

b.

c.

d.

e.

f.

SCORE [   ]

CAPÍTULO 2

II. Reading

B. Match each question on the left with the most appropriate answer on the right. (14 points)

_____ 7. ¿Qué hay en tu cuarto?

_____ 8. ¿Tiene Martín un escritorio en su cuarto?

_____ 9. ¿Tiene Marta un televisor?

_____ 10. ¿Hay una ventana en tu cuarto?

_____ 11. ¿Hay un televisor en tu cuarto?

_____ 12. ¿Cuántos carteles tienes?

_____ 13. ¿Tienes muchos libros?

a. Sí, hay muchas ventanas en mi cuarto.
b. Sí, tiene un escritorio.
c. Hay una cama y un escritorio.
d. Tengo cuatro carteles.
e. Sí, en mi cuarto hay un televisor.
f. No, no tengo libros.
g. No, no tiene televisor.

SCORE [   ]

Quiz 2-2B

III. Writing

C. Complete this conversation between Paco and his friend Miguel. Use the cues in parentheses to write what they say. (12 points)

PACO   Oye, Miguel, ¿cuántos carteles tienes en tu cuarto?

14.   MIGUEL   _____ (many)

15.   PACO   _____

MIGUEL   Tengo catorce revistas.

PACO   ¿Y tienes una lámpara en tu cuarto?

16.   MIGUEL   _____ (2)

PACO   ¿Y un televisor? ¿Hay televisor en tu cuarto?

17.   MIGUEL   _____ (1)

SCORE ☐

IV. Culture

D. Imagine you are an exchange student living in Madrid, Spain. Would you make the following comments in a letter to your family? Write *likely* or *unlikely* for each comment. (3 points)

18.   I'm living in an apartment.

_____

19.   I have a phone in my room.

_____

20.   There are TVs in every room.

_____

SCORE ☐

TOTAL SCORE ☐ /35

CAPÍTULO 2

CAPÍTULO 2

¡Organízate!

Quiz 2-3A

■ TERCER PASO

Maximum Score: 30

Grammar and Vocabulary

A. Read the sentences, then indicate what each person needs to do for that situation or problem. (8 points)

_____ 1. Martín has books, papers, and CDs all over his room.

_____ 2. Yamila wants some new clothes for school.

_____ 3. Eduardo needs school supplies, a watch, and some new sneakers.

_____ 4. Teresa has three assignments due tomorrow.

_____ 5. Pablo's clothes are all over his bedroom floor.

_____ 6. Andrea is a new student, and doesn't know anyone.

_____ 7. Tomás is really hungry.

_____ 8. Lucía can't find the money her mom gave her in her purse.

a. hacer la tarea
b. ir al centro comercial
c. organizar el cuarto
d. encontrar el dinero
e. comprar muchas cosas
f. conocer a muchos amigos nuevos
g. poner la ropa en el armario
h. ir a la pizzería

SCORE _____

B. Raquel and Víctor are talking after school. Complete their conversation with the missing words from the box. (9 points)

| quieres | hacer la tarea | Quiero | ir a la pizzería | organizar |
| | necesitas | poner | encontrar | comprar muchas cosas |

RAQUEL Víctor, ¿qué quieres hacer?

VÍCTOR **9.** _____ ir al centro comercial. Necesito **10.** _____.

RAQUEL ¿Qué cosas **11.** _____ comprar?

VÍCTOR Muchas cosas para mis clases y mi cuarto. ¿Y qué **12.** _____ hacer tú?

RAQUEL Pues, yo quiero **13.** _____ . Me gusta mucho la pizza. Pero necesito **14.** _____ mi dinero primero.

VÍCTOR ¿Tienes mucha tarea? ¿Quieres **15.** _____ después (*afterwards*)?

RAQUEL Sí, buena idea. Pero antes (*before*), necesito **16.** _____ mi cuarto.

VÍCTOR Yo también. Necesito **17.** _____ mucha ropa en el armario.

SCORE _____

Quiz 2-3A

C. Explain to Rafael how much money he needs to buy the following things. Write out all numbers. (8 points)

18. tres carteles/$38.00 _____

19. un armario/$165.00 _____

20. un televisor/$199.00 _____

21. unas zapatillas de tenis/$76.00 _____

22. una radio/$53.00 _____

23. un diccionario español-inglés/$47.00 _____

24. un escritorio/$121.00 _____

25. una silla/$64.00 _____

SCORE [ ]

D. Complete the statements by writing out the numbers in parentheses as words. (5 points)

26. Hay _____ (151) estudiantes en las clases de español.

27. Paco tiene _____ (21) dólares en su mochila.

28. Hay _____ (31) mesas en la cafetería.

29. Necesito _____ (81) dólares para comprar unas zapatillas de tenis.

30. Hay _____ (41) revistas en el cuarto de Miguel.

SCORE [ ]

TOTAL SCORE [/30]

CAPÍTULO 2

2 ¡Organízate!

Quiz 2-3B

■ TERCER PASO

Maximum Score: 30

I. Listening

A. Tomás is telling you what he wants and needs to do today. Write the letter of the sentence in the blank next to the picture it matches. (8 points)

 1. _____

 3. _____

 2. _____

 4. _____

SCORE [   ]

II. Reading

B. Elena and Mateo are talking after school. Put their scrambled conversation in order from **a** to **f**. (6 points)

_____ 5. Hola, Mateo. ¿Qué tal?

_____ 6. Sí, quiero ir, pero necesito organizar mi cuarto primero.

_____ 7. Bueno, porque *(because)* necesito encontrar mi dinero.

_____ 8. ¿Por qué *(Why?)* necesitas organizar tu cuarto?

_____ 9. Bien, gracias. ¿Qué quieres hacer?

_____ 10. Quiero ir al centro comercial para comprar unas zapatillas de tenis. ¿Quieres ir?

SCORE [   ]

Quiz 2-3B

III. Writing

C. Based on the drawing, write two sentences explaining what Juanjo needs to do and two sentences saying what he wants to do. (16 points)

11. _____

12. _____

13. _____

14. _____

SCORE [   ]

TOTAL SCORE [   ] /30

CUMULATIVE SCORE FOR QUIZZES 1–3 [   ] /100

CAPÍTULO 2

CAPÍTULO

2

¡Organízate!

Chapter 2 Test

I. Listening

Maximum Score: 30 points

A. Listen to the conversation between Ana and Miguel. Based on their dialogue, select the phrase that tells what Miguel wants or needs. (10 points)

_____ 1. **a.** un televisor
b. una radio
c. una radio y un televisor

_____ 2. **a.** un cuaderno
b. un libro
c. un libro y un cuaderno

_____ 3. **a.** unos lápices
b. unos bolígrafos
c. unos lápices y unos bolígrafos

_____ 4. **a.** un teléfono
b. unos carteles
c. un teléfono y unos carteles

_____ 5. **a.** un libro de español
b. una goma de borrar
c. un libro de español y una goma de borrar

SCORE _____

B. Felipe and Andrea are at a meeting of international students. Based on their conversation, write **a) sí**, or **b) no** for the English statements which follow. (20 points)

_____ 6. Felipe and Andrea have known each other for a long time.

_____ 7. Felipe and Andrea are from the same country.

_____ 8. Andrea is from Mexico.

_____ 9. Felipe is from Spain.

_____ 10. Andrea doesn't want to go to the mall.

_____ 11. Andrea needs to do her homework.

_____ 12. Andrea only needs to straighten up her room.

_____ 13. Felipe doesn't need to do his homework.

_____ 14. Felipe needs a new backpack.

_____ 15. Andrea doesn't go with Felipe.

SCORE _____

CAPÍTULO 2

Chapter 2 Test

II. Reading

Maximum Score: 30 points

C. Luis is writing a letter to a pen pal. Read his letter and decide if the statements below describe Luis correctly or not. Write **a) sí** or **b) no** in each blank. (10 points)

Hola,

Me llamo Luis y soy de la capital de los Estados Unidos. Tengo dieciséis años. Me gustan muchas cosas. Me gusta el fútbol y me gusta la música rock. No me gusta la comida italiana, pero me gusta mucho la comida china. Me gusta mucho la escuela. Mi clase favorita es la clase de matemáticas, y para la clase necesito una regla y una calculadora. Ya tengo una calculadora pero una regla no. Para la clase de inglés, necesito un cuaderno y papel, pero una goma de borrar no. Hay veinticinco profesores en la escuela y muy buena comida en la cafetería. ¿A ti te gusta la escuela?

Hasta luego,

Luis

_____ 16. Luis knows exactly what supplies he needs for each class.

_____ 17. Luis would rather go to an Italian restaurant than to school.

_____ 18. Luis is a well-rounded person with many interests.

_____ 19. Luis has everything he needs for math class.

_____ 20. Luis doesn't like the school cafeteria.

SCORE

D. Match the following questions in column A with the correct answer in column B. (10 points)

Column A

_____ 21. ¿Necesitas un cuaderno?

_____ 22. ¿Qué quieres hacer hoy?

_____ 23. ¿Cuánto dinero tienes?

_____ 24. ¿Quieres ir al centro comercial?

_____ 25. ¿Hay un televisor en tu cuarto?

Column B

a. Sí, pero necesito organizar mi cuarto.
b. No tengo mucho.
c. No, ya tengo un cuaderno.
d. Quiero comprar unas zapatillas de tenis.
e. No, no hay.

SCORE [   ]

E. Five students each won $100 to buy things for school and their rooms. They listed what they want to buy with their prize money. Match each student's list with his or her purchases. (10 points)

a. b. c. d. e.

26. _____ Quiero comprar ropa, unos carteles y una radio.

27. _____ Para mis clases, necesito una calculadora y unas zapatillas de tenis.

28. _____ Quiero comprar ropa y un televisor para mi cuarto.

29. _____ Pues, yo quiero muchas cosas: una calculadora, un reloj, una mochila y unas revistas.

30. _____ Yo necesito unos carteles para mi cuarto. También necesito un reloj y un diccionario.

SCORE [   ]

CAPÍTULO 2

Chapter 2 Test

III. Culture

Maximum Score: 10 points

F. Read the statements below. Based on the information in your textbook, write **a) cierto** or **b) falso** in each blank. (10 points)

_____ 31. Students in Spanish-speaking countries sometimes must buy a school uniform.

_____ 32. Often sisters or brothers in Spain share a bedroom in an apartment.

_____ 33. It's uncommon for students in Spanish-speaking countries to carry book bags or backpacks.

_____ 34. Spanish and Latin American households typically have one television set for the whole family.

_____ 35. Students in Spain and Latin America often carry their supplies to school daily because they do not have lockers.

SCORE _____

CAPÍTULO 2

IV. Writing

Maximum Score: 30 points

G. Write two sentences saying what there is in Débora's room and three sentences saying what she needs to do. (15 points)

36. _____

37. _____

38. _____

39. _____

40. _____

SCORE ☐

Chapter 2 Test

H. Express the following questions in Spanish. Write all numbers as words. (15 points)

How would you tell a friend . . .?

41. you have 100 dollars

_____

42. you need to buy some posters

_____

43. you have 21 magazines

_____

How would you ask a friend . . .

44. how many books he or she needs to buy?

¿_____?

45. if he or she has a lot of classes?

¿_____?

SCORE _____

TOTAL SCORE _____ /100

CAPÍTULO 2

CAPÍTULO 2 Chapter Test Score Sheet

Circle the letter that matches the most appropriate response.

I. Listening
Maximum Score: 30 points

A. (10 points)

1. a b c
2. a b c
3. a b c
4. a b c
5. a b c

SCORE [   ]

B. (20 points)

6. a b
7. a b
8. a b
9. a b
10. a b

11. a b
12. a b
13. a b
14. a b
15. a b

SCORE [   ]

II. Reading
Maximum Score: 30 points

C. (10 points)

16. a b
17. a b
18. a b
19. a b
20. a b

SCORE [   ]

D. (10 points)

21. a b c d e
22. a b c d e
23. a b c d e
24. a b c d e
25. a b c d e

SCORE [   ]

E. (10 points)

26. a b c d e
27. a b c d e
28. a b c d e
29. a b c d e
30. a b c d e

SCORE [   ]

CAPÍTULO 2

III. Culture

Maximum Score: 10 points

F. (10 points)

31. a b

32. a b

33. a b

34. a b

35. a b

SCORE [____]

IV. Writing

Maximum Score: 30 points

G. (15 points)

36. _____

37. _____

38. _____

39. _____

40. _____

SCORE [____]

H. (15 points)

41. _____

42. _____

43. _____

44. _____

45. _____

SCORE [____]

TOTAL SCORE [____ /100]

CAPITULO 2

Scripts for Quizzes 2-1B, 2-2B, 2-3B

Quiz 2-1B Capítulo 2 Primer paso

I. Listening

A.   CLARA   No tengo bolígrafo y no tengo libro. Pero tengo dos calculadoras y muchas gomas de borrar. También tengo un diccionario en mi mochila.

Quiz 2-2B Capítulo 2 Segundo paso

I. Listening

A. 1.   DAVID   Luisa, ¿qué tienes en tu cuarto?
          LUISA   Tengo una cama, una mesa y una lámpara.
    2.   DAVID   Pedro, ¿qué hay en tu cuarto?
          PEDRO   Hay un escritorio y muchos carteles.
    3.   DAVID   Alicia, ¿tienes un televisor en tu cuarto?
          ALICIA   No, no tengo televisor. Tengo una radio.
    4.   DAVID   Carlos, ¿tienes un reloj?
          CARLOS   Sí, tengo un reloj.
    5.   MARTA   Ana, ¿qué hay en tu cuarto?
          ANA   Hay un televisor.
    6.   DAVID   Juan, ¿cuántos libros hay en tu cuarto?
          JUAN   Hay muchos libros.

Quiz 2-3B Capítulo 2 Tercer paso

I. Listening

A.   a. Hoy necesito hacer la tarea.
     b. Quiero comprar zapatillas de tenis nuevas.
     c. Necesito organizar mi cuarto.
     d. Quiero ir al centro comercial.

CAPÍTULO 2

ANSWERS Quiz 2-1A

A. (7 points: 1 point per item)
1. regla
2. calculadora
3. mochila
4. diccionario
5. bolígrafo
6. carpeta
7. papel

B. (8 points: 1 point per item)
8. una, un
9. una, una
10. una, un
11. un, una

C. (12 points: 2 points per item)
12. unos papeles
13. unas gomas
14. unos libros
15. unos lápices
16. unos cuadernos
17. unas carpetas

D. (8 points: 1 point per item)
18. Yo
19. él
20. tú
21. Ella
22. Yo
23. Ella
24. Él
25. Tú

ANSWERS Quiz 2-1B

I. Listening

A. (10 points: 2 points per item)
1. no
2. no
3. sí
4. sí
5. sí

II. Reading

B. (10 points: 2 points per item)
6. Casa del Libro
7. Papelería Ferrer
8. Notebooks, paper
9. Casa del Libro
10. Papelería Ferrer; calculator and ruler

III. Writing

C. (10 points: 2 points per item)
11. Él necesita un cuaderno.
12. Él necesita papel.
13. Él necesita un diccionario/un libro.
14. Ella necesita una calculadora.
15. Ella necesita unos lápices.

IV. Culture

D. (5 points: 2.5 points per item)
16. a
17. b

ANSWERS Quiz 2-2A

A. (9 points: 1 point per item)
1. cuarto
2. una cama
3. un armario
4. una silla
5. una lámpara
6. ventanas
7. una puerta
8. una radio
9. unos carteles

B. (12 points: 2 points per item)
10. Hay dieciocho armarios.
11. Hay veinticinco relojes.
12. Hay veintiuna camas.
13. Hay doce escritorios.
14. Hay quince mesas.
15. Hay treinta televisores.

C. (14 points: 2 points per item)
16. Cuántas
17. muchos
18. Cuántas
19. muchos
20. mucha
21. Cuántos
22. muchas

ANSWERS Quiz 2-2B

I. Listening

A. (6 points: 1 point per item)
1. f
2. c
3. a
4. e
5. b
6. d

II. Reading

B. (14 points: 2 points per item)
7. c
8. b
9. g
10. a
11. e
12. d
13. f

III. Writing

C. (12 points: 3 points per item)
14. Tengo muchos carteles en mi cuarto.
15. ¿Cuántas revistas tienes en tu cuarto?
16. Sí, tengo dos lámparas.
17. Sí, hay un televisor.

IV. Culture

D. (3 points: 1 point per item)
18. likely
19. unlikely
20. unlikely

CAPÍTULO 2

Answers to Quizzes 2-3A, 2-3B

ANSWERS Quiz 2-3A

A. (8 points: 1 point per item)
1. c
2. b
3. e
4. a
5. g
6. f
7. h
8. d

B. (9 points: 1 point per item)
9. Quiero
10. comprar muchas cosas
11. necesitas/quieres
12. quieres/necesitas
13. ir a la pizzería
14. encontrar
15. hacer la tarea
16. organizar
17. poner

C. (8 points: 1 point per item)
18. treinta y ocho dólares
19. ciento sesenta y cinco dólares
20. ciento noventa y nueve dólares
21. setenta y seis dólares
22. cincuenta y tres dólares
23. cuarenta y siete dólares
24. ciento veintiún dólares
25. sesenta y cuatro dólares

D. (5 points: 1 point per item)
26. ciento cincuenta y un
27. veintiún
28. treinta y una
29. ochenta y ún
30. cuarenta y una

ANSWERS Quiz 2-3B

I. Listening

A. (8 points: 2 points per item)
1. a
2. d
3. c
4. b

II. Reading

B. (6 points: 1 point per item)
5. a
6. d
7. f
8. e
9. b
10. c

III. Writing

C. (16 points: 4 points per item)
Answers may vary. Possible answers:
11. Juanjo necesita organizar su cuarto.
12. Juanjo necesita hacer la tarea.
13. Juanjo quiere encontrar el dinero.
14. Juanjo quiere comprar zapatillas de tenis.

Scripts for Chapter 2 Test

I. Listening

A. 1. ANA   ¿Quieres un televisor o una radio?
       MIGUEL   Quiero un televisor; ya tengo una radio.
2. ANA   ¿Qué necesitas para la clase de inglés?
       MIGUEL   Necesito un libro pero ya tengo un cuaderno.
3. ANA   ¿Necesitas unos lápices?
       MIGUEL   Sí, y también unos bolígrafos.
4. ANA   ¿Qué quieres para tu cuarto?
       MIGUEL   Quiero un teléfono y unos carteles.
5. ANA   ¿Necesitas una goma de borrar para la clase de español?
       MIGUEL   No, pero necesito un libro de español.

B. FELIPE   Hola, me llamo Felipe. Y tú, ¿cómo te llamas?
    ANDREA   Me llamo Andrea. Soy de México. ¿Y tú?
    FELIPE   Soy de España. ¿Quieres ir al centro comercial?
    ANDREA   Sí, pero, necesito organizar mi cuarto y hacer la tarea.
    FELIPE   Sí, yo también necesito hacer la tarea, pero también necesito comprar una mochila.
    ANDREA   Bueno, tengo que irme.
    FELIPE   Pues, hasta luego, Andrea.
    ANDREA   Adiós, Felipe. Hasta pronto.

CAPÍTULO 2

Answers to Chapter 2 Test

I. Listening Maximum Score: 30 points

A. (10 points: 2 points per item)
1. a
2. b
3. c
4. c
5. a

B. (20 points: 2 points per item)
6. b
7. b
8. a
9. a
10. b
11. a
12. b
13. b
14. a
15. a

II. Reading Maximum Score: 30 points

C. (10 points: 2 points per item)
16. a
17. b
18. a
19. b
20. b

D. (10 points: 2 points per item)
21. c
22. d
23. b
24. a
25. e

E. (10 points: 2 points per item)
26. c
27. b
28. e
29. d
30. a

III. Culture Maximum Score: 10 points

F. (10 points: 2 points per item)
31. a
32. a
33. b
34. a
35. a

IV. Writing Maximum Score: 30 points

G. (15 points: 3 points per item)
Answers will vary. Possible answers:
36. Tiene un escritorio en su cuarto.
37. Hay una ventana en su cuarto.
38. Débora necesita organizar su cuarto.
39. Débora necesita poner la ropa en el armario.
40. Débora necesita hacer la tarea.

H. (15 points: 3 points per item)
41. Tengo cien dólares.
42. Necesito comprar unos carteles.
43. Tengo veintiuna revistas.
44. ¿Cuántos libros necesitas comprar?
45. ¿Tienes muchas clases?

3

Nuevas clases, nuevos amigos

■ PRIMER PASO

Maximum Score: 35

Grammar and Vocabulary

A. Complete the sentences about what classes people have this afternoon with the missing Spanish words. (8 points)

1. Juliana tiene _____ (*English*) y _____ (*art*).

2. Mi amigo Eduardo tiene _____ (*geography*) y _____ (*social studies*).

3. Tengo _____ (*computer science*).

4. ¿Tienes _____ (*math*) también?

5. Yolanda tiene _____ (*science*) y _____ (*physical education*).

SCORE [   ]

B. Marisela is running late, and her mom is helping her get ready for school. Complete their conversation with the correct definite articles. (15 points)

MAMÁ   Marisela, es tarde. Ya son las ocho. ¿Tienes _____ mochila y
                6.

        _____ libros?
        7.

MARISELA   Sí, mamá. Pero... ¿dónde están _____ carpetas para
                    8.

        _____ clases de inglés y francés?
        9.

MAMÁ   Están aquí, en la mesa. ¿Y qué más necesitas? ¿_____
                              10.

        cuadernos? ¿_____ zapatillas de tenis?
                 11.

MARISELA   Sí, y también necesito _____ tarea y _____
                      12.   **13.**

        almuerzo.

MAMÁ   Bien. ¿Tienes _____ carteles para tu clase de arte?
                    14.

MARISELA   Sí. Y también necesito _____ revistas para mi clase de inglés.
                      15.

SCORE [   ]

Quiz 3-1A

III. Writing

C. Read what class Claudia has right now, then write a sentence explaining what time it is. Use the information in Claudia's schedule. (12 points)

Hora	Clase
8:00	Ciencias sociales
8:55	Francés
9:40	Descanso
10:05	Química
10:45	Computación
11:30	Geografía
12:50	Educación física
13:25	Inglés

16. Tiene francés ahora (*now*). _____

17. Ahora tiene la clase de computación. _____

18. Necesita ir a la clase de educación física ahora. _____

19. Su clase de geografía es ahora. _____

20. Tiene inglés ahora. _____

21. Ahora tiene la clase de química. _____

SCORE [   ]

TOTAL SCORE [   ] /35

CAPÍTULO 3

Nuevas clases, nuevos amigos

Quiz 3-1B

Maximum Score: 35

■ PRIMER PASO

I. Listening

A. Look at the clocks and listen to the brief dialogues that follow. Write the letter that corresponds to the clock that shows the time you hear. Not all of the clocks will be used. (10 points)

a.

b.

c.

d.

e.

f.

1. _____   2. _____   3. _____   4. _____   5. _____

SCORE ☐

II. Reading

B. Pablo and Paulina are discussing their class schedules. Put their conversation in the correct order from **a** to **e**. (10 points)

_____ 6. No, pero mañana sí.

_____ 7. Tengo geografía y por fin computación. Y tú, Paulina, ¿tienes computación hoy?

_____ 8. Bueno, primero tengo matemáticas, después tengo francés.

_____ 9. Pablo, ¿qué clases tienes hoy?

_____ 10. ¿Y luego?

SCORE ☐

Quiz 3-1 B

III. Writing

C. Study Luisa's class schedule and read the statements about her activities at different times during the day. For each activity, write a sentence in Spanish explaining what time it is and what class Luisa has. Spell out all numbers. (10 points)

hora	8:05	9:15	10:25	11:45	12:30	1:10	2:20
clase	computación	español	ciencias	inglés	almuerzo	educación física	ciencias sociales

11. Luisa is doing a chemistry experiment.

   _____

12. She's playing volleyball.

   _____

13. She is reading a short story by Ernest Hemingway.

   _____

14. Luisa is researching on the Internet.

   _____

15. She's saying "Buenos días" to her teacher.

   _____

SCORE [   ]

IV. Culture

D. Read each of the following statements. Based on the information in your textbook, fill in each blank with **a) cierto** or **b) falso**. (5 points)

_____ 16. In Mexico, a grade of 6 is considered passing.

_____ 17. In Peru, a grade of 16 on a test would be considered low.

SCORE [   ]

TOTAL SCORE [   ] /35

Spanish 1 ¡Ven conmigo!, Chapter 3

CAPÍTULO 3

CAPÍTULO 3

Nuevas clases, nuevos amigos

SEGUNDO PASO

Maximum Score: 30

Grammar and Vocabulary

A. Write a sentence explaining at what time the classes and events below take place, using the cues given. Spell out all numbers as words. (12 points)

1. la clase de inglés (12:30 p.m.) _____

2. el concierto de jazz (7:45 p.m.) _____

3. la clase de computación (8:20 a.m.) _____

4. el almuerzo (1:00 p.m.) _____

5. la fiesta (9:15 p.m) _____

6. la clase de matemáticas (10:10 a.m.) _____

7. el programa de televisión (5:30 p.m.) _____

8. el descanso (2:50 p.m.) _____

SCORE [   ]

B. Explain at what time you want or need to do the following activities. Begin your sentences with **Necesito…** or **Quiero…** and mention a different time for each activity. Remember to explain if the activity will take place in the morning, afternoon, or evening. (12 points)

9. ir a la clase de español _____

10. hacer la tarea _____

11. ir al centro comercial _____

12. organizar mi cuarto _____

13. poner la ropa en el armario _____

14. ir a la pizzería con amigos _____

SCORE [   ]

Quiz3-2A

C. Everyone brought in props for the class play, and now they're all mixed up. Explain to whom each prop belongs, using the list below. (6 points)

15.	**reloj**	el profesor Iriarte
16.	**ropa**	Teresa
17.	**televisor**	la profesora Guillén
18.	**calculadora**	el director Sastre
19.	**pizza**	el estudiante nuevo
20.	**zapatillas de tenis**	Ricardo

15. _____

16. _____

17. _____

18. _____

19. _____

20. _____

SCORE [   ]

TOTAL SCORE [   ] /30

Spanish 1 ¡Ven conmigo!, Chapter 3

CAPÍTULO 3

3

Nuevas clases, nuevos amigos

Quiz 3-2B

SEGUNDO PASO

Maximum Score: 30

I. Listening

A. Some friends are talking about their classes and class schedules. Choose the best answer to the question that you hear from the choices below. (8 points)

_____ 1. **a.** Son las diez y cuarto.
   b. Es a las nueve y media.
   c. No tengo clase de español.

_____ 2. **a.** La clase de matemáticas es a las tres.
   b. Me gusta más el béisbol.
   c. La clase de español es a las ocho.

_____ 3. **a.** Tengo la clase de educación física a las dos.
   b. Luego, tengo la clase de arte.
   c. A las once en punto.

_____ 4. **a.** Sí, tengo una clase de ciencias este año.
   b. Sí, mi clase de francés es a la una.
   c. No, ya tengo unas zapatillas de tenis.

SCORE [   ]

II. Reading

B. Eva and Leo are both taking Spanish, but their classtimes, teachers, and classrooms are different. Look over the information about their classes, and then decide whether the statements that follow are **a) cierto** or **b) falso**. (12 points)

Eva	Leo
8:45 A.M.	3:20 P.M.
Profesora Obregón	Profesor Peña
Sala 14	Sala 12

_____ 5. La clase de Eva es a las nueve y cuarto de la mañana.

_____ 6. Son las nueve menos diez de la mañana. Eva está atrasada.

_____ 7. El profesor de Leo se llama Profesor Peña.

_____ 8. Son las tres y dieciocho de la tarde. Leo tiene prisa.

_____ 9. Profesora Obregón es la profesora de Eva.

_____ 10. La clase de Leo es en la sala número dos.

SCORE [   ]

Quiz 3-2B

III. Writing

C. For each picture, write a sentence in Spanish to answer the question below. Be sure to give the name of each class and to say whether it is in the morning or afternoon. Write all clock times as words. (6 points)

MODELO   ¿A qué hora es la clase?

11._____   12._____   13._____

_____   _____   _____

_____   _____   _____

SCORE [   ]

IV. Culture

D. Read each of the following statements and, based on the information in your textbook, answer with **a) cierto** or **b) falso**. (4 points)

_____ **14.** In Spanish-speaking countries, if you arrived up to one hour later than you were told for work, you would not really be considered late.

_____ **15.** In Spanish-speaking countries, students' schedules vary from day to day.

SCORE [   ]

TOTAL SCORE [   ] /30

Spanish 1 ¡Ven conmigo!, Chapter 3

CAPÍTULO 3

CAPÍTULO 3

Nuevas clases, nuevos amigos

TERCER PASO

Grammar and Vocabulary

A. Disagree with everything your friends say by writing the opposite of their opinions. Remember to use the correct form of the adjective. (12 points)

1. El colegio es feo. _____
2. La directora es simpática. _____
3. Las clases son malas. _____
4. Los estudiantes son aburridos. _____
5. La cafetería es pequeña. _____
6. La tarea es fácil. _____
7. El profesor es bajo. _____
8. La profesora es rubia. _____

SCORE [____]

B. Below are a series of descriptions of some of the people and things at school. Match each subject with its correct description. (8 points)

_____ 9. Es grande, nuevo y bonito.
_____ 10. Es aburrida y difícil.
_____ 11. Son inteligentes y simpáticas.
_____ 12. Es nueva y pequeña.
_____ 13. Son grandes y muy bonitos.
_____ 14. Es estricto pero interesante.
_____ 15. Son muy cómicos y simpáticos.
_____ 16. Es muy mala.

a. los carteles
b. la comida de la cafetería
c. mis amigos
d. la tarea
e. la radio
f. el colegio
g. el profesor
h. Mónica y Marta

SCORE [____]

CAPÍTULO 3

Quiz 3-3A

C. Read what you and some classmates want to do this weekend. Then explain what each person likes, using the words in the box below and the correct form of **gustar**. (7.5 points)

> **las novelas**   **los deportes**   **las fiestas**   **los conciertos**   **los videojuegos**

17. Ricardo quiere ir a una fiesta.

_____

18. Yo quiero ir a la librería.

_____

19. Antonio quiere comprar un videojuego nuevo.

_____

20. Sandra quiere jugar (*to play*) al voleibol y al tenis.

_____

21. Tú quieres ir al concierto, ¿verdad?

_____

SCORE _____

D. You want to find out more about the new student Alicia. Ask your friend if Alicia likes the following things. Use tag questions and the correct form of **gustar**. (7.5 points)

22. el colegio _____

23. las fiestas _____

24. la comida mexicana _____

25. los partidos _____

26. los bailes _____

SCORE _____

TOTAL SCORE _____ /35

Spanish 1 ¡Ven conmigo!, Chapter 3

CAPÍTULO 3

3 Nuevas clases, nuevos amigos

■ TERCER PASO

Maximum Score: 35

I. Listening

A. Listen as María and Flori describe some of their friends. Write the letter of the picture that they describe. (10 points)

a.

b.

c.

d.

e.

1. _____ 2. _____ 3. _____ 4. _____ 5. _____

SCORE [   ]

Quiz 3-3B

II. Reading

B. Read the results of a survey your classmates took to find out which subjects everyone likes and dislikes. Then write the name of the student most likely to have made the statements that follow. (10 points)

Clase	Yoli	Damián
¿Te gusta la clase de historia?	sí	no
¿Te gusta la clase de geografía?	no	sí
¿Te gusta la clase de computación?	no	sí
¿Te gusta la clase de educación física?	sí	no

_____ 6. ¡Uf! La clase de geografía es muy aburrida y difícil.

_____ 7. Me gustan mucho los deportes, especialmente el volibol y el baloncesto.

_____ 8. Hay mucha tarea en la clase de historia, y el profesor es muy estricto.

_____ 9. Mis compañeros en la clase de computación son muy simpáticos.

_____ 10. La profesora de mi clase de historia es inteligente y divertida.

SCORE _____

III. Writing

C. Tell your family what school is like this year by completing the sentences with the correct form of the verb **ser** and the correct Spanish form of the adjective in parentheses. (15 points)

11. La clase de francés _____ _____ (*boring*).

12. Los compañeros en mi clase de matemáticas _____ _____ (*funny*).

13. La profesora de inglés _____ _____ (*strict*) y _____ (*disagreeable*).

14. Mis amigos y yo _____ muy _____ (*intelligent*).

Now explain what subjects you and your classmates like by completing the sentences with the correct pronoun and form of **gustar**. (6 points)

15. Mi clase favorita es español. _____ _____ mucho la profesora.

16. A Alicia no _____ _____ las ciencias.

17. A Jacobo _____ _____ mucho la computación.

SCORE _____

TOTAL SCORE _____ /35

CUMULATIVE SCORE FOR QUIZZES 1–3 _____ /100

CAPÍTULO 3

Nuevas clases, nuevos amigos

I. Listening

Maximum Score: 30 points

A. You will hear statements describing the pictures. Write the letter that corresponds to the picture that is described. (10 points)

a.

b.

c.

d.

HORARIO		
8:30-9:30	francés	Profesora Bermondy
9:30-10:30	química	Profesor Peña
10:30-10:45	descanso	
10:45-11:45	coro	Profesor Méndez
11:45-12:15	almuerzo	
12:15-1:15	computación	Profesora Soto
1:15-1:30	descanso	
1:30-2:30	geografía	Profesora Smith
2:30-3:30	español	Profesor Galindo

e.

1. _____

2. _____

3. _____

4. _____

5. _____

SCORE [ ]

CAPÍTULO 3

Chapter 3 Test

B. Look over the statements below carefully. Then listen to the conversation between Bernardo and Lupita. Indicate if the statement is **a) true**, or **b) false**. (20 points)

_____ **6.** La clase de ciencias es muy aburrida.

_____ **7.** La clase de arte es a las seis.

_____ **8.** La clase de geografía es la clase favorita de Lupita.

_____ **9.** A Bernardo le gustan los partidos de béisbol.

_____ **10.** A Bernardo le gustan los videojuegos.

_____ **11.** A Lupita le gustan los videojuegos.

_____ **12.** A Lupita no le gustan los conciertos.

_____ **13.** A Bernardo no le gustan los conciertos.

_____ **14.** Bernardo y Lupita quieren ir a un concierto.

_____ **15.** El concierto es a las ocho menos cuarto.

SCORE _____

II. Reading

Maximum Score: 30 points

C. Read the following paragraph about María Elena's schedule. Then read the sentences that follow and write **a) cierto** or **b) falso** for each statement. (10 points)

> Tengo muchas clases este año. Primero, tengo geografía a las nueve menos cuarto. Es una clase muy interesante con una profesora estricta pero simpática. Luego, a las diez y cuarto, tengo la clase de francés, que es muy aburrida; me gusta más la clase de español. Pero hay un chico rubio y muy guapo en la clase de francés. A él le gusta la clase de francés. Mis amigas y yo comemos (*eat*) en la cafetería de la escuela a las doce. A mi amiga Tanya le gusta la comida en la cafetería. La comida allí es muy mala. Por la tarde, tengo inglés y educación física. No me gusta la clase de educación física porque es a las tres y veinte de la tarde.

_____ **16.** María Elena likes all of her classes.

_____ **17.** She has French after geography and before lunch.

_____ **18.** María Elena doesn't like her geography teacher.

_____ **19.** María Elena doesn't like eating in the cafeteria.

_____ **20.** There is a good-looking student in María Elena's Spanish class.

SCORE _____

CAPÍTULO 3

Chapter 3 Test

D. Beto has four classes today. Arrange the statements below in the correct chronological order. (10 points)

    a. Primero tiene la clase de español, a las nueve de la mañana.
    b. A las tres de la tarde, tiene la clase de ciencias sociales.
    c. Después del almuerzo, tiene un descanso.
    d. Luego, a las doce, es la hora del almuerzo.
    e. A las diez y media tiene la clase de matemáticas.

21. _____

22. _____

23. _____

24. _____

25. _____

SCORE _____

E. According to Gloria's schedule, decide whether the statements that follow are **a) cierto** or **b) falso**. (10 points)

Hora	Clase
8:10	música
9:05	matemáticas
10:10	descanso
10:20	computación
11:15	inglés
12:05	almuerzo
1:00	arte
1:50	historia
2:40	ciencias

CAPÍTULO 3

Chapter 3 Test

_____ **26.** Gloria tiene nueve clases hoy.

_____ **27.** Por la tarde, primero tiene la clase de arte, después historia y luego ciencias.

_____ **28.** Su clase de historia es a las dos y diez de la tarde.

_____ **29.** Son las diez menos veinte de la mañana. Gloria tiene prisa porque la clase de computación es ahora.

_____ **30.** Son las ocho de la mañana en punto. Gloria no está atrasada para la clase de música.

SCORE _____

III. Culture

Maximum Score: 8 points

F. Read the statements below and indicate if they are **a) cierto** or **b) falso**. (8 points)

_____ **31.** All Spanish-speaking students go to school from 7 A.M. to 2 P.M. every day.

_____ **32.** In Peru, a grade of 12 is considered passing.

_____ **33.** Arriving late for a party is considered acceptable in many Spanish-speaking countries.

_____ **34.** Students in Spanish-speaking countries may take as many as nine different courses.

SCORE _____

CAPÍTULO 3

IV. Writing

Maximum Score: 32 points

G. Write one sentence in Spanish for each of the following. (20 points)

35. Use three adjectives to describe yourself.

_____

_____

_____

36. Use two adjectives to describe your friends.

_____

_____

_____

37. State one class that you like and one that you don't like.

_____

_____

_____

38. Explain why you like and don't like the classes you mentioned above.

_____

_____

_____

39. Write a sentence telling a friend you have to go because you're in a hurry.

_____

_____

_____

SCORE [   ]

CAPÍTULO 3

Chapter 3 Test

H. Look at the timepieces below and express what time it is in Spanish. Write out all numbers as words. (12 points)

(A.M.)

40. _____

(P.M.)

41. _____

(P.M.)

42. _____

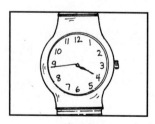

(P.M.)

43. _____

SCORE _____

TOTAL SCORE _____ /100

Spanish 1 ¡Ven conmigo!, Chapter 3

CAPÍTULO 3 Chapter Test Score Sheet

Circle the letter that matches the most appropriate response.

I. Listening

Maximum Score: 30 points

A. (10 points)

1. a b c d e
2. a b c d e
3. a b c d e
4. a b c d e
5. a b c d e

SCORE [   ]

B. (20 points)

6. a b
7. a b
8. a b
9. a b
10. a b

11. a b
12. a b
13. a b
14. a b
15. a b

SCORE [   ]

II. Reading

Maximum Score: 30 points

C. (10 points)

16. a b
17. a b
18. a b
19. a b
20. a b

SCORE [   ]

D. (10 points)

21. a b c d e
22. a b c d e
23. a b c d e
24. a b c d e
25. a b c d e

SCORE [   ]

E. (10 points)

26. a b
27. a b
28. a b
29. a b
30. a b

SCORE [   ]

III. Culture

Maximum Score: 8 points

F. (8 points)

31. a b
32. a b
33. a b
34. a b

SCORE [   ]

CAPÍTULO 3

IV. Writing

G. (20 points)

35. _____
_____
_____

36. _____
_____
_____

37. _____
_____
_____

38. _____
_____
_____

39. _____
_____
_____

SCORE [　　　]

H. (12 points)

40. _____

41. _____

42. _____

43. _____

SCORE [　　　]

TOTAL SCORE [　　/100]

Spanish 1 ¡Ven conmigo!, Chapter 3

CAPÍTULO 3

Scripts for Quizzes 3-1B, 3-2B, 3-3B

Quiz 3-1B Capítulo 3 Primer paso

I. Listening

A.
1. —¿Qué hora es, señorita?
   —Son las cuatro y cuarto.
2. —Perdón, ¿qué hora es?
   —Son las nueve y media.
3. —Por favor, señor, ¿qué hora es?
   —Son las ocho menos diez.
4. —Buenas tardes, Guillermo. ¿Qué hora es?
   —Son las cuatro y media.
5. —Hola, señor, ¿qué hora es?
   —Son las doce menos cuarto.

Quiz 3-2B Capítulo 3 Segundo paso

I. Listening

A.
1. ¿A qué hora es la clase de inglés?
2. ¿A qué hora tienes la clase de español?
3. ¿Cuándo tienes la clase de música?
4. ¿Tienes una clase de francés?

Quiz 3-3B Capítulo 3 Tercer paso

I. Listening

A.
1. Luis y Tomás son altos y rubios.
2. Luisa es una chica muy bonita.
3. Ellas son morenas y bajas.
4. El señor García es muy estricto pero simpático.
5. Mis amigos son divertidos.

ANSWERS Quiz 3-1A

A. (8 points: 1 point per item)
1. inglés, arte
2. geografía, ciencias sociales
3. computación
4. matemáticas
5. ciencias, educación física

B. (15 points: 1.5 points per item)
6. la
7. los
8. las
9. las
10. Los
11. Las
12. la
13. el
14. los
15. las

C. (12 points: 2 points per item)
16. Son las nueve menos cinco.
17. Son las once menos cuarto.
18. Es la una menos diez.
19. Son las once y media.
20. Es la una y veinticinco.
21. Son las diez y cinco.

ANSWERS Quiz 3-1B

I. Listening

A. (10 points: 2 points per item)
1. a
2. e
3. d
4. c
5. b

II. Reading

B. (10 points: 2 points per item)
6. e
7. d
8. b
9. a
10. c

III. Writing

C. (10 points: 2 points per item)
11. Son las diez y veinticinco. Ella tiene ciencias.
12. Es la una y diez. Ella tiene educación física.
13. Son las doce menos cuarto. Ella tiene inglés.
14. Son las ocho y cinco. Ella tiene computación.
15. Son las nueve y cuarto. Ella tiene español.

IV. Culture

D. (5 points: 2.5 points per item)
16. a
17. b

CAPÍTULO 3

Answers to Quizzes 3-2A, 3-2B

ANSWERS Quiz 3-2A

A. (12 points: 1.5 points per item)
1. Es a las doce y media de la tarde.
2. Es a las ocho menos cuarto de la noche.
3. Es a las ocho y veinte de la mañana.
4. Es a la una en punto de la tarde.
5. Es a las nueve y cuarto de la noche.
6. Es a las diez y diez de la mañana.
7. Es a las cinco y media de la tarde.
8. Es a las tres menos diez de tarde.

B. (12 points: 2 points per item)
Answers will vary. Possible answers:
9. Necesito ir a la clase de español a las diez y doce de la mañana.
10. Necesito hacer la tarea a las ocho y media de la noche.
11. Quiero ir al centro comercial a las tres de la tarde.
12. Necesito organizar mi cuarto a las cinco y cuarto de la tarde.
13. Necesito poner la ropa en el armario a las siete y media de la noche.
14. Quiero ir a la pizzería con amigos a las seis de la tarde.

C. (6 points: 1 point per item)
15. El reloj es del profesor Iriarte.
16. La ropa es de Teresa.
17. El televisor es de la profesora Guillén.
18. La calculadora es del director Sastre.
19. La pizza es del estudiante nuevo.
20. Las zapatillas de tenis son de Ricardo.

ANSWERS Quiz 3-2B

I. Listening

A. (8 points: 2 points per item)
1. b
2. c
3. c
4. b

II. Reading

B. (12 points: 2 points per item)
5. b
6. a
7. a
8. a
9. a
10. b

III. Writing

C. (6 points: 2 points per item)
11. La clase de ciencias es a la una y diez de la tarde.
12. La clase de educación física es a las diez y media de la mañana.
13. La clase de computación es a las doce.

IV. Culture

D. (4 points: 2 points per item)
14. b
15. a

CAPÍTULO 3

ANSWERS Quiz 3-3A

A. (12 points: 1.5 points per item)
1. El colegio es bonito.
2. La directora es antipática.
3. Las clases son buenas.
4. Los estudiantes son interesantes.
5. La cafetería es grande.
6. La tarea es difícil.
7. El profesor es alto.
8. La profesora es morena.

B. (8 points: 1 point per item)
9. f
10. d
11. h
12. e
13. a
14. g
15. c
16. b

C. (7.5 points: 1.5 points per item)
17. Le gustan las fiestas.
18. Me gustan las novelas.
19. Le gustan los videojuegos.
20. Le gustan los deportes.
21. ¿Te gustan los conciertos?

D. (7.5 points: 1.5 points per item)
22. A Alicia le gusta el colegio, ¿verdad?/¿no?
23. A Alicia le gustan las fiestas, ¿verdad?/¿no?
24. A Alicia le gusta la comida mexicana, ¿verdad?/¿no?
25. A Alicia le gustan los partidos, ¿verdad?/¿no?
26. A Alicia le gustan los bailes, ¿verdad?/¿no?

ANSWERS Quiz 3-3B

I. Listening

A. (10 points: 2 points per item)
1. b
2. c
3. a
4. d
5. e

II. Reading

B. (10 points: 2 points per item)
6. Yoli
7. Yoli
8. Damián
9. Damián
10. Yoli

III. Writing

C. (15 points: 1 point per item)
11. es, aburrida
12. son, cómicos/divertidos
13. es, estricta, antipática
14. somos, inteligentes
15. Me, gusta
16. le, gustan
17. le, gusta

CAPÍTULO 3

Scripts for Chapter 3 Test

I. Listening

A.
1. Son las dos y cuarto y voy a la clase de educación física.
2. ¿Qué clases tiene Pedro?
3. Mi clase favorita es el francés.
4. Mi clase de arte es muy aburrida.
5. Mis amigas son altas.

B.

BERNARDO	¡Hola! Me llamo Bernardo. Tengo nuevas clases este semestre. Tengo clases de geografía, inglés, ciencias y arte. La clase de ciencias es muy interesante.
LUPITA	¿A qué hora es tu clase de arte?
BERNARDO	Es a la una y veinte. Y tú, ¿qué clases tienes?
LUPITA	Tengo clases de geografía, español, computación y ciencias. Mi clase favorita es la clase de geografía. Bernardo, ¿te gustan los partidos de béisbol?
BERNARDO	Sí, me gustan, pero me gustan más los videojuegos porque son interesantes. ¿Te gustan?
LUPITA	No, no me gustan porque son aburridos, pero me gustan los conciertos. Son muy divertidos.
BERNARDO	A mí también me gustan. ¿Quieres ir a un concierto mañana a las ocho y media?
LUPITA	Sí, quiero ir. Vamos a las ocho menos cuarto.
BERNARDO	Bueno, hasta luego.

I. Listening   Maximum Score: 30 points

A. (10 points: 2 points per item)   **B.** (20 points: 2 points per item)

1. c	6. b	11. b
2. e	7. b	12. b
3. d	8. a	13. b
4. b	9. a	14. a
5. a	10. a	15. b

II. Reading   Maximum Score: 30 points

C. (10 points: 2 points per item)   **D.** (10 points: 2 points per item)   **E.** (10 points: 2 points per item)

16. b	21. a	26. b
17. a	22. e	27. a
18. b	23. d	28. b
19. a	24. c	29. b
20. b	25. b	30. a

III. Culture   Maximum Score: 8 points

F. (8 points: 2 points per item)

31. b
32. a
33. a
34. a

IV. Writing   Maximum Score: 32 points

G. (20 points: 4 points per item)
Answers will vary. Possible answers:
35. Soy interesante, inteligente y cómico.
36. Mis amigos son divertidos y cómicos.
37. Me gusta la clase de matemáticas y no me gusta la clase de geografía.
38. Me gusta porque es interesante y no me gusta porque es aburrida.
39. Tengo que irme porque tengo prisa.

H. (12 points: 3 points per item)
40. Son las doce menos cuarto de la mañana.
41. Es la una y media de la tarde.
42. Son las seis y veintitrés de la noche.
43. Son las cuatro menos dieciséis de la tarde.

Spanish 1 ¡Ven conmigo!, Chapter 3

Nombre _____ Clase _____ Fecha _____

CAPÍTULO

4 ¿Qué haces esta tarde?

Quiz 4-1A

Maximum Score: 35

■ PRIMER PASO

Grammar and Vocabulary

A. Discuss what you and your friends like to do in your free time. Using the drawings, write a sentence or question with the correct form of **gustar**. (10 points)

1. José Alberto   2. Carmiña   3. yo   4. Marcia   5. tú

1. _____

2. _____

3. _____

4. _____

5. ¿_____?

SCORE _____

B. Inés is explaining how she and her family spend a typical Saturday. Complete her description with the correct form of the missing verbs. Each verb will be used only once. (15 points)

descansar	preparar	cuidar	tomar	hablar
hacer	mirar	pasar	lavar	caminar

Por la mañana, organizo mi cuarto. Rafael y papá _____ el carro y mamá
                                                      6.
_____ a mi hermanito Sergio. Luego, mamá y yo _____ con el perro en el
      7.   8.
parque. A veces papá _____ un partido de fútbol en la televisión. También él
                          9.
_____ el rato con sus amigos en el café. Más tarde, Rafael y yo _____ la cena
      10.   11.
y mamá _____ en su cuarto. Después de cenar, yo _____ un helado con mis
            12.   13.
amigas, o _____ por teléfono. ¿Y tú? ¿Qué _____ en el tiempo libre?
              14.   15.

SCORE _____

Quiz 4-1A

C. Complete the sentences about who does free-time activities together with **con** and the correct pronoun. Remember that *with me* and *with you* have special forms. (5 points)

16. Por la tarde, Susana trabaja en un restaurante. Yo trabajo _____ .

17. Montas en bicicleta hoy, ¿verdad? ¿Quién monta en bicicleta _____ ?

18. Me gusta hablar por teléfono, y a Martín le gusta también. Él habla

    _____ mucho.

19. Después de clases, Clara necesita ir al centro comercial. Quiero ir _____ .

20. Por la tarde, papá prepara la cena. Necesito preparar la cena _____ .

SCORE [   ]

D. Explain to your new neighbor Patricio who the different members of the Peña family are. Use the word **que** to connect the two parts of your sentences, and use a different verb in each sentence. (5 points)

MODELO   La persona que escucha música es Beatriz.

21. Florencia   22. doña Mari   25. don Jaime   23. David   24. Beatriz

21. _____

22. _____

23. _____

24. _____

25. _____

SCORE [   ]

TOTAL SCORE [/35]

Spanish 1 ¡Ven conmigo!, Chapter 4

4 ¿Qué haces esta tarde?

Quiz 4-1 B

■ PRIMER PASO

Maximum Score: 35

I. Listening

A. Listen to Pilar tell you what her friends do. Match her statements to the appropriate pictures. (10 points)

a.   b.   c.   d.   e.

1. _____   2. _____   3. _____   4. _____   5. _____

SCORE [   ]

II. Reading

B. Read what Raúl does after school and during his free time. Respond to the statements that follow with **sí** or **no**. (10 points)

> Después de clases practico el piano y la guitarra. Me gusta tocar el piano, pero no me gusta tocar la guitarra. Luego camino con mi perro Héctor en el parque. A Héctor le gusta ir al parque conmigo. Después paso el rato con amigos. Cuando regreso a casa, saco la basura y preparo la cena. Luego, estudio y escucho música.

_____ 6. Raúl likes playing the guitar.

_____ 7. Héctor likes going to the park alone.

_____ 8. Raúl usually goes for a walk on the beach.

_____ 9. Raúl avoids doing chores at home.

_____ 10. Raúl listens to music after fixing dinner.

SCORE [   ]

Quiz 4-1 B

III. Writing

C. You are interviewing Eugenio. Write a question asking him what he likes to do after school. Then write Eugenio's answer telling what each person in the following scenes likes to do. Write one sentence in Spanish for each picture. (10 points)

12.

13.

14.

15.

Eugenio   Carmela   David   Marcos

11. ¿_____?

12. _____

13. _____

14. _____

15. _____

SCORE [   ]

IV. Culture

D. Based on the information in your textbook about the 2000 Olympic Games, complete the following. (5 points)

16. Name at least one gold-medal winning country. _____

17. Name at least three sports in which Spanish speakers won any Olympic medal.

_____   _____   _____

18. Name at least one Spanish-speaking athlete who won an Olympic medal.

_____

SCORE [   ]

TOTAL SCORE [   ] /35

Spanish 1 ¡Ven conmigo!, Chapter 4

4 ¿Qué haces esta tarde?

■ SEGUNDO PASO

Quiz 4-2A

Maximum Score: 35

Grammar and Vocabulary

A. Delia calls her friend Lydia after school. Complete their conversation with the correct forms of the verb **estar**. (12 points)

DELIA   Hola, Lydia. Soy yo, Delia.

LYDIA   Delia, hola. ¿Qué tal? ¿_____ en casa ahora?
1.

DELIA   No, _____ en el centro, con Tere y Rubén. Nosotros _____ en la
2.   3.

pizzería.

LYDIA   ¿_____ ustedes en la pizzería al lado del parque?
4.

DELIA   No, en la pizzería que _____ al lado del gimnasio. Oye, ¿quieres ir con
5.

nosotros ahora a tomar un helado?

LYDIA   Sí, quiero ir, pero es imposible. Ahora yo _____ en casa con mi hermanito.
6.

Oye, Delia, ¿_____ Lucila allí con ustedes?
7.

DELIA   No, ella y Jorge _____ en la plaza.   SCORE [   ]
8.

B. Read what different people are doing, then write a sentence explaining what place each person or group is in right now. Use subject pronouns, the correct form of **estar**, and a different place in each sentence. (14 points)

restaurante	biblioteca	piscina	supermercado	casa	gimnasio	tienda

9. Wilfredo compra comida para la cena.

_____

10. Lavo los platos y después saco la basura.

_____

11. Rosa y sus amigas nadan.

_____

Quiz 4-2A

12. Miriam y Salvador estudian para un examen.

_____

13. Arturo y yo compramos ropa.

_____

14. Joaquín sirve (*serves*) comida mexicana a muchas personas.

_____

15. Tú y Leonor practican el baloncesto.

_____

SCORE [   ]

C. Answer the questions about what everyone does after school. Use subject pronouns and the correct form of the infinitives given in your answers. (9 points)

16. ¿Qué hace Guillermo después de clases? (tocar la guitarra)

_____

17. ¿Y Leonardo y Martín? (mirar la televisión)

_____

18. ¿Y tú? (trabajar en un restaurante)

_____

19. ¿Y Margarita y Brenda? (bailar con un grupo de baile)

_____

20. ¿Y tú y Maribel? (pasar el rato con amigos)

_____

21. ¿Y la profesora? (escuchar música)

_____

SCORE [   ]

TOTAL SCORE [   ] /35

¿Qué haces esta tarde?

Quiz 4-2B

Maximum Score: 35

■ SEGUNDO PASO

I. Listening

A. Listen as María tells you what she sees. Match her statements to the appropriate pictures. (10 points)

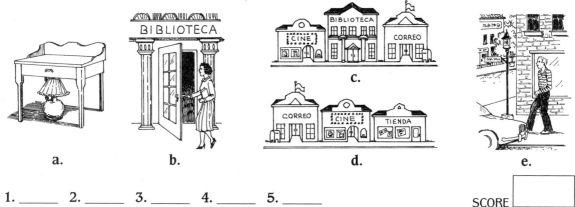

a.   b.   c.   d.   e.

1. _____   2. _____   3. _____   4. _____   5. _____   SCORE [   ]

II. Reading

B. Indicate whether the statements below are **a) cierto** or **b) falso** based on the map. (10 points)

_____ 6. El supermercado está encima del gimnasio.

_____ 7. La tienda está debajo de la librería.

_____ 8. El gimnasio está lejos de la librería.

_____ 9. El restaurante está al lado del supermercado.

_____ 10. El restaurante está cerca del cine.

SCORE [   ]

Quiz 4-2B

III. Writing

C. All the people below are doing things in their free time. Indicate where they are by writing a Spanish sentence with the correct form of **estar** and a logical place. Use subject pronouns in your sentences. (10 points)

11. Marisa y Tomás caminan con el perro.

_____

12. Luisa y Ana toman un refresco.

_____

13. Alberto, preparas la cena ahora, ¿verdad?

_____

14. Maricela y yo nadamos.

_____

15. Juan practica el baloncesto.

_____

SCORE ☐

IV. Culture

D. Read the following brief exchange and then answer the questions in English. (5 points)

SRA. RAMÍREZ   Buenos días, Pablo. ¿Cómo estás hoy?
     PABLO   Muy bien. ¿Cómo está usted?
SRA. RAMÍREZ   Muy bien, gracias, Pablo. Hasta luego.
     PABLO   Adiós.

16. Why does Pablo address señora Ramírez as **usted** and not **tú**?

_____

_____

17. Who would Pablo appropriately address as **tú**?

_____

_____

SCORE ☐

TOTAL SCORE ☐ /35

CAPÍTULO 4

¿Qué haces esta tarde?

■ TERCER PASO

Grammar and Vocabulary

A. Complete Yolanda's note to her friend with the correct form of the verb **ir**. (9 points)

¿Qué haces esta tarde? Tengo mucha tarea, y primero _____ a casa para estudiar.
                                                        1.

Después quiero _____ al café para tomar un refresco. Tú _____
                          2.   3.

conmigo, ¿verdad? Teresa no _____ porque tiene clase de arte. Pero mañana ella y
                                      4.

yo _____ al cine. Tú y Josué _____ también, ¿no?
                  5.   6.

SCORE [ ]

B. Use the correct form of **ir** and **para** + *infinitive* to explain where everyone is going today, and what they are going to do at those places. For each place, choose a different, logical infinitive from the list. (12 points)

MODELO   Fernando/casa
              Fernando va a casa para descansar.

estudiar   montar en bicicleta   tomar un refresco   comprar comida
ver una película   tomar una clase de baile   comprar ropa   nadar

  7. mis amigos y yo/café _____

  8. Blanca y Gabriela/cine _____

  9. Papá/supermercado _____

10. tú/biblioteca _____

11. yo/parque _____

12. Héctor/piscina _____

13. tú y Victoria/gimnasio _____

14. mis amigos/tienda _____

SCORE [ ]

Quiz 4-3A

CAPÍTULO 4

C. Your friend is writing a letter to a pen pal in Mexico about her schedule, and needs your help with some sentences. Write the Spanish equivalents for the missing words. (9 points)

15. _____, tengo un examen de historia.
    On Monday

16. _____, voy a mi clase de piano.
    On Tuesdays

17. _____, quiero ir al cine.
    On Friday

18. _____, necesito cuidar a mi hermanita.
    On Thursdays

19. _____, voy a un restaurante con mi familia.
    On Saturday

20. _____, siempre descanso.
    On the weekends

SCORE [____]

TOTAL SCORE [____ /30]

Nombre _____ Clase _____ Fecha _____

4 ¿Qué haces esta tarde?

Quiz 4-3B

TERCER PASO

Maximum Score: 30

I. Listening

A. Carlos and Ana are discussing where various people are going. Listen to their conversation and write the letter of the place that each person is going. (5 points)

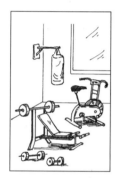    

   a.   b.   c.   d.   e.

_____ 1. Luis   _____ 2. Ana   _____ 3. Pedro   _____ 4. Carlos   _____ 5. la señora Méndez

SCORE [ ]

II. Reading

B. Lorena has a lot of activities planned this week. Look over her calendar, then answer the questions that follow. Write your answers in Spanish. (10 points)

lunes	martes	miércoles	jueves	viernes	sábado	domingo
biblioteca gimnasio	trabajo— restaurante	centro comercial con Diana	trabajo— restaurante	partido de fútbol	parque con Sergio fiesta para José 9:00	biblioteca

6. What days does Lorena work? _____

7. What days will she study? _____

8. What day will she probably go bike riding? _____

9. What day will she buy an outfit for the party? _____

10. What day is her karate class? _____

SCORE [ ]

Quiz 4-3B

CAPÍTULO 4

III. Writing

C. Look at the illustrations. How would you ask Eduardo where he is going after school today? How would he answer for himself and Tomás? How would Eduardo tell you where his friends and teachers are going? (10 points)

12.

Tomás y Eduardo

13.

Alicia y Estrella

14.

el profesor Montoya y
la profesora Salazar

15.

Martín

11. ¿ _____

_____ ?

12. _____

_____

13. _____

_____

14. _____

_____

15. _____

_____

SCORE [ ]

IV. Culture

D. Based on the information in your textbook, respond **sí** or **no** to the following statements. (5 points)

_____ **16.** In Spain and Latin America, there are fewer school-sponsored extracurricular activities for high school students than in the United States.

_____ **17.** Teenagers in Spanish-speaking countries who play sports will often join school teams since most schools have their own teams.

SCORE [ ]

TOTAL SCORE [/30]

CUMULATIVE SCORE FOR QUIZZES 1–3 [/100]

Spanish 1 ¡Ven conmigo!, Chapter 4

CAPÍTULO

4

¿Qué haces esta tarde?

Chapter 4 Test

I. Listening

Maximum Score: 30 points

A. Juana is looking at the map below and is telling Jorge where several buildings are, but she has made some mistakes. If her statements are accurate according to the map, answer **a) sí**; if not, answer **b) no**. (15 points)

1. _____
2. _____
3. _____
4. _____
5. _____

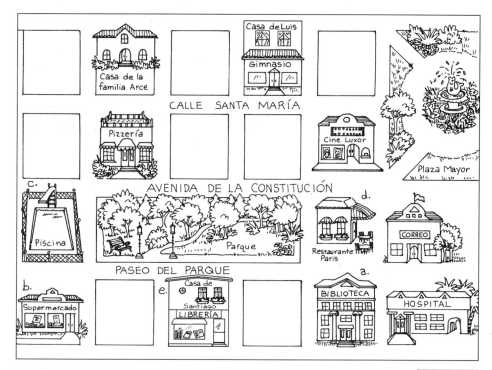

SCORE ☐

B. Juana is now telling Jorge what people like to do or where they are going. Using the same map above, write the letter of the place that she refers to in her statements. (15 points)

6. _____
7. _____
8. _____
9. _____
10. _____

SCORE ☐

Chapter 4 Test

II. Reading

Maximum Score: 30 points

C. Julio is a very busy teenager. Read the description of his activities for this weekend. Answer the questions that follow with **a) sí** or **b) no**. (15 points)

Hoy es viernes, y después de clases escucho música y hablo por teléfono con mi amiga Esmeralda. El sábado en la mañana, saco la basura y camino con el perro en el parque. No me gusta sacar la basura pero me gusta caminar con mi perro. Él es muy cómico. Por la tarde tomo refrescos con mis amigos y voy al centro comercial para comprar un videojuego. En la noche, preparo la cena para mi familia. A mi mamá no le gusta preparar la comida los sábados. Después, mi amiga Esmeralda y yo vamos al cine para ver una película muy divertida. El domingo, voy a la biblioteca para estudiar. No me gusta estudiar los domingos, pero tengo mucha tarea. Luego, regreso a casa y descanso un rato.

_____ 11. A Julio no le gustan los animales.

_____ 12. Julio va al correo los sábados.

_____ 13. Julio lava el carro antes de preparar la cena.

_____ 14. A Esmeralda le gusta ir al cine.

_____ 15. A Julio no le gusta hacer la tarea los domingos.

SCORE [____]

Chapter 4 Test

D. Read the following ads for pen pals. Match the students on the left with those on the right who have common activities and interests. (15 points)

_____ 16. **Óscar**   A mí me gustan los deportes, especialmente el baloncesto y el voleibol. Voy al gimnasio después de clases.

_____ 17. **Miguel**   Me gusta la música. Después de clases, canto en el coro, voy a mi clase de música o practico el piano.

_____ 18. **Beatriz**   Me gusta ir al parque en mi tiempo libre. Allí monto en bicicleta o camino con mi perro.

_____ 19. **Patricia**   No tengo mucho tiempo libre, porque trabajo en la tienda de mis padres después de clases. Me gusta ir al café y pasar el rato con mis amigos.

_____ 20. **Jazmín**   Me gusta el arte muchísimo. En mi tiempo libre, voy a una clase de arte. Me gusta dibujar y pintar.

a. Laura   Montar en bicicleta es mi deporte favorito. Este año, quiero una bicicleta nueva. Y me gustan mucho los animales.

b. Jacobo   A mí me gusta estar con mis amigos. Me gusta hablar por teléfono con ellos o ir a tomar un helado con ellos.

c. Fátima   Trabajo en una piscina después de clases. Me gusta la natación, y me gusta ir al gimnasio.

d. Leonor   Me gusta ir a la bibioteca en mi tiempo libre y ver los libros de arte. También me gusta ir al museo de arte.

e. Alonso   Escucho música o practico la guitarra en mi tiempo libre. También trabajo en una tienda de música.

SCORE [ ]

CAPÍTULO 4

Chapter 4 Test

III. Culture

Maximum Score: 16 points

E. Indicate whether the following statements are **a) cierto** or **b) falso** based on the information in your textbook. (12 points)

_____ **21.** High schools in Spanish-speaking countries do not normally have school-sponsored athletics and students join independent sports teams.

_____ **22.** In many Spanish-speaking countries, it is common for children to address their parents as **usted**.

_____ **23.** Few Latin American countries send teams to participate in the Olympics.

_____ **24.** It's always appropriate to use **tú** when addressing a person you don't know.

SCORE [   ]

F. Explain what the **paseo** is and tell what purpose it serves in Spanish-speaking countries. (4 points)

25. _____

_____

_____

_____

_____

_____

_____

_____

SCORE [   ]

Chapter 4 Test

IV. Writing   Maximum Score: 24 points

G. Gaby is explaining what she does during a typical week. Complete her sentences below with the correct form of the verb in parentheses. (12 points)

26. En el colegio, primero yo _____ a la clase de inglés. (ir)

27. Después, Sergio y yo _____ en el coro. (cantar)

28. Luego, tengo una clase de arte con Toño. Nosotros _____ frutas y otras cosas. (dibujar)

29. Después de clases, yo _____ al Café Nueva York. (caminar)

30. Mis amigos _____ refrescos allá casi todos los días. (tomar)

31. Cuando regreso a casa mi hermanito y yo _____ la televisión. (mirar)

32. Mamá no _____ en casa. (estar)

33. Ella y Papá _____ hasta las seis. (trabajar)

34. Después de la cena, mi hermanito _____ los platos. (lavar)

35. Los fines de semana mi amigo Manuel y yo _____ a una fiesta o al cine. (ir)

36. Él _____ muy bien. (bailar)

37. Y tú, ¿adónde _____ los fines de semana? (ir)

SCORE [   ]

H. Your Chilean pen pal, Santiago, asked what you do during the week. Write six sentences in Spanish giving him the information below. (12 points)

Write a sentence telling him . . .

38. on Mondays you take out the trash.

_____

39. on Tuesdays you go to the library.

_____

40. on Wednesdays you walk the dog before school.

_____

Chapter 4 Test

CAPÍTULO 4

41. on Thursdays you swim in the gym after school.

_____

42. on Fridays you go to the movie theater.

_____

43. on weekends you practice the piano and spend time with friends.

_____

SCORE ☐

TOTAL SCORE ☐ /100

Spanish 1 ¡Ven conmigo!, Chapter 4

Nombre _____ Clase _____ Fecha _____

Circle the letter that matches the most appropriate response.

I. Listening
Maximum Score: 30 points

A. (15 points)　　　　　　**B.** (15 points)

1. a b　　　　　　6. a b c d e
2. a b　　　　　　7. a b c d e
3. a b　　　　　　8. a b c d e
4. a b　　　　　　9. a b c d e
5. a b　　　　　　10. a b c d e

SCORE [＿＿＿]　　SCORE [＿＿＿]

II. Reading
Maximum Score: 30 points

C. (15 points)　　　　　　**D.** (15 points)

11. a b　　　　　　16. a b c d e
12. a b　　　　　　17. a b c d e
13. a b　　　　　　18. a b c d e
14. a b　　　　　　19. a b c d e
15. a b　　　　　　20. a b c d e

SCORE [＿＿＿]　　SCORE [＿＿＿]

III. Culture
Maximum Score: 16 points

E. (12 points)　　　　　　**F.** (4 points)

21. a b　　　　　　25. _____
22. a b　　　　　　_____
23. a b　　　　　　_____
24. a b　　　　　　_____

SCORE [＿＿＿]　　　　　　　　　　SCORE [＿＿＿]

Spanish 1 ¡Ven conmigo!, Chapter 4　　　　　　Testing Program **97**

IV. Writing

Maximum Score: 24 points

G. (12 points)

26. _____

27. _____

28. _____

29. _____

30. _____

31. _____

32. _____

33. _____

34. _____

35. _____

36. _____

37. _____

SCORE [   ]

H. (12 points)

38. _____

_____

39. _____

_____

40. _____

_____

41. _____

_____

42. _____

_____

43. _____

_____

SCORE [   ]

TOTAL SCORE [/100]

Spanish 1 ¡Ven conmigo!, Chapter 4

CAPÍTULO 4

Scripts for Quizzes 4-1B, 4-2B, 4-3B

Quiz 4-1B Capítulo 4 Primer paso

I. Listening

A. 1. Marta escucha música por la noche.
    2. Miguel pinta muy bien.
    3. Javier, Beto y Pablo practican el fútbol.
    4. Mis amigos montan en bicicleta.
    5. Al señor Morales le gusta lavar la ropa.

Quiz 4-2B Capítulo 4 Segundo paso

I. Listening

A. 1. La lámpara está debajo del escritorio.
    2. El cine está al lado del correo.
    3. La biblioteca está al lado del correo.
    4. Pablo está en el centro.
    5. Luisa va a estudiar.

Quiz 4-3B Capítulo 4 Tercer paso

I. Listening

A. 1. CARLOS   ¿Adónde va Luis?
        ANA   Va al cine para mirar la película nueva.
    2. CARLOS   Y tú, Ana, ¿adónde vas?
        ANA   Voy al gimnasio.
    3. CARLOS   ¿Va al cine Pedro?
        ANA   No, va a la piscina porque le gusta nadar.
    4.   ANA   Y tú, Carlos, ¿adónde vas ahora?
        CARLOS Ya son las tres y media; voy a casa.
    5.   ANA   ¿La señora Méndez?
        CARLOS Necesita comprar estampillas. Va al correo.

CAPÍTULO 4

ANSWERS Quiz 4-1A

A. (10 points: 2 points per item)
1. A José Alberto le gusta nadar.
2. A Carmiña le gusta montar en bicicleta.
3. A mí me gusta tocar el piano.
4. A Marcia le gusta pintar.
5. ¿Te gusta escuchar música?

B. (15 points: 1.5 points per item)
6. lavan
7. cuida
8. caminamos
9. mira
10. pasa
11. preparamos
12. descansa
13. tomo
14. hablo
15. haces

C. (5 points: 1 point per item)
16. con ella
17. contigo
18. conmigo
19. con ella
20. con él

D. (5 points: 1 point per item)
21. La persona que pinta es Florencia.
22. La persona que mira la televisión es doña Mari.
23. La persona que saca la basura es David.
24. La persona que lava el carro es Beatriz.
25. La persona que lava la ropa es don Jaime.

ANSWERS Quiz 4-1B

I. Listening

A. (10 points: 2 points per item)
1. e   2. a   3. c   4. b   5. d

II. Reading

B. (10 points: 2 points per item)
6. no
7. no
8. no
9. no
10. sí

III. Writing

C. (10 points: 2 points per item)
11. ¿Qué te gusta hacer después de clases?
12. A mí me gusta jugar al fútbol.
13. A Carmela le gusta tocar la guitarra.
14. A David le gusta jugar al tenis.
15. A Marcos le gusta tocar el piano.

IV. Culture

D. (5 points: 1 point per correct name)
16. *any one of the following:* Spain, Mexico, Cuba
17. *any three of the following:* weightlifting, boxing, (women's) volleyball, swimming, sailing, judo, cycling, gymnastics
18. *any one of the following:* María Urrutia, Soraya Jiménez, Isabel Fernández, Juan Llaneras, Claudia Poll, Carlos Espínola, Serena Amato, Gervasio Deferr

ANSWERS Quiz 4-2A

A. (12 points: 1.5 points per item)
1. Estás
2. estoy
3. estamos
4. Están
5. está
6. estoy
7. está
8. están

B. (14 points: 2 points per item)
9. Él está en el supermercado.
10. Yo estoy/tú estás en casa.
11. Ellas están en la piscina.
12. Ellos están en la biblioteca.
13. Nosotros estamos en la tienda.
14. Él está en el restaurante.
15. Ustedes están en el gimnasio.

C. (9 points: 1.5 points per item)
16. Él toca la guitarra.
17. Ellos miran la televisión.
18. Yo trabajo en un restaurante.
19. Ellas bailan con un grupo de baile.
20. Nosotros/Nosotras pasamos el rato con amigos.
21. Ella escucha música.

ANSWERS Quiz 4-2B

I. Listening
A. (10 points: 2 points per item)
1. a   2. d   3. c   4. e   5. b

II. Reading
B. (10 points: 2 points per item)
6. b   7. b   8. a   9. b   10. a

III. Writing
C. (10 points: 2 points per item)
Answers will vary. Possible answers:
11. Ellos están en el parque.
12. Ellas están en el café.
13. Tú estás en casa.
14. Nosotros/Nosotras estamos en la piscina.
15. Él está en el gimnasio.

IV. Culture
D. (5 points: 2.5 points per item)
16. **Usted** is the appropriate form of address for people you want to show respect to or people you don't know well.
17. Pablo can use **tú** with anyone he knows well, someone his own age, or anyone he's on a first-name basis with.

Answers to Quizzes 4-3A, 4-3B

ANSWERS Quiz 4-3A

A. (9 points: 1.5 points per item)
1. voy
2. ir
3. vas
4. va
5. vamos
6. van

B. (12 points: 1.5 points per item)
7. Mis amigos y yo vamos al café para tomar un refresco.
8. Blanca y Gabriela van al cine para ver una película.
9. Papá va al supermercado para comprar comida.
10. Vas a la biblioteca para estudiar.
11. Voy al parque para montar en bicicleta.
12. Héctor va a la piscina para nadar.
13. Tú y Victoria van al gimnasio para tomar una clase de baile.
14. Mis amigos van a la tienda para comprar ropa.

C. (9 points: 1.5 points per item)
15. El lunes
16. Los martes
17. El viernes
18. Los jueves
19. El sábado
20. Los fines de semana

ANSWERS Quiz 4-3B

I. Listening
A. (5 points: 1 point per item)
1. e   2. a   3. c   4. b   5. d

II. Reading
B. (10 points: 2 points per item)
6. el martes y el jueves
7. el lunes y el domingo
8. el sábado
9. el miércoles
10. el lunes

III. Writing
C. (10 points: 2 points per item)
Answers will vary. Possible answers:
11. ¿Adónde vas después de clases?
12. Tomás y yo vamos al gimnasio.
13. Alicia y Estrella van a la biblioteca.
14. El profesor Montoya y la profesora Salazar van a un restaurante.
15. Martín va al supermercado.

IV. Culture
D. (5 points: 2.5 points per item)
16. sí
17. no

Spanish 1 ¡Ven conmigo!, Chapter 4

I. Listening

    A. 1. El correo está al lado del supermercado.

          2. La biblioteca está cerca del correo.

          3. El gimnasio está encima de la casa de Luis.

          4. El hospital está lejos de la pizzería.

          5. La librería está debajo de la casa de Santiago.

    B. 6. Tomás va a tomar refrescos con sus amigos.

          7. María y Luisa necesitan comprar libros de arte.

          8. Beto quiere comprar comida para el perro.

          9. A los niños les gusta nadar.

        10. María Inés necesita estudiar.

Answers to Chapter 4 Test

I. Listening Maximum Score: 30 points

A. (15 points: 3 points per item)
1. b
2. a
3. b
4. a
5. a

B. (15 points: 3 points per item)
6. d
7. e
8. b
9. c
10. a

II. Reading Maximum Score: 30 points

C. (15 points: 3 points per item)
11. b
12. b
13. b
14. a
15. a

D. (15 points: 3 points per item)
16. c
17. e
18. a
19. b
20. d

III. Culture Maximum Score: 16 points

E. (12 points: 3 points per item)
21. a
22. a
23. b
24. b

F. (4 points)
25. Answers will vary. Possible answer: The **paseo** is a tradition in Spanish-speaking countries in which friends and relatives get together in small groups and spend time together in the park, walking downtown, or in their neighborhood. It gives people a chance to be together, to socialize, to talk about what's going on in their lives and in their world.

IV. Writing Maximum Score: 24 points

G. (12 points: 1 point per item)
26. voy
27. cantamos
28. dibujamos
29. camino
30. toman
31. miramos
32. está
33. trabajan
34. lava
35. vamos
36. baila
37. vas

H. (12 points: 2 points per item)
38. Los lunes saco la basura.
39. Los martes voy a la biblioteca.
40. Los miércoles camino con el perro antes de clases.
41. Los jueves nado en el gimnasio después de clases.
42. Los viernes voy al cine.
43. Los fines de semana practico el piano y paso el rato con amigos.

El ritmo de la vida

▦ **PRIMER PASO**

Grammar and Vocabulary

A. Sandra is interviewing her classmate Martín about his daily routine. Complete their conversation with the missing expressions from the box. Use a different expression for each blank. (8 points)

todavía	**muchas veces**	**siempre**	**durante la semana**
sólo cuando	**todos los días**	**con qué frecuencia**	**a veces**

SANDRA   Martín, ¿cómo es una semana típica para ti?

MARTÍN   Pues, _____ hago muchas cosas. Voy a clase, al trabajo y al gimnasio.
1.

SANDRA   ¿Y _____ vas al gimnasio? ¿Un día, dos días, tres días...?
2.

MARTÍN   Voy allí _____ después de clases, y los fines de semana también. Me
3.

gusta mucho ir al gimnasio.

SANDRA   ¿Y _____ vas con tus amigos?
4.

MARTÍN   No siempre, pero sí _____ mis amigos van conmigo para jugar al baloncesto.
5.

SANDRA   ¿Y _____ nadas en la piscina también?
6.

MARTÍN   Sí, me gusta nadar, pero _____ tengo tiempo.
7.

SANDRA   ¿Y _____ trabajas todas las noches?
8.

MARTÍN   No, ahora trabajo sólo los lunes y los jueves.   SCORE [   ]

B. Answer the questions about Julia and her daily routine, using negative words such as **no, nadie, nada**, and **nunca**. (9 points)

9. ¿Qué quiere comprar Julia para su cuarto? _____

10. ¿Siempre estudia ella los fines de semana? _____

11. ¿Con quién va ella al centro comercial? _____

12. ¿Qué necesita comprar Julia para las clases? _____

13. ¿Cuándo cuida a su hermanita? _____

14. ¿Quién camina con ella en el parque? _____

SCORE [   ]

CAPÍTULO 5

Quiz 5-1A

C. Gilberto leads a very boring life. Complete his description of a typical week with the correct missing negative words: **no, nadie, nada, nunca**. Some of the words may be used more than once. (8 points)

_____ hago _____ durante la semana. Después de clases,
  15.   16.

_____ voy al parque con mis amigos. Voy a casa, pero _____ miro la
   17.   18.

televisión. Sólo hago la tarea, pero _____ estudia conmigo. _____
                                         19.   20.

hablo por teléfono. Los fines de semana también son muy aburridos. A veces voy al gimnasio o

al cine, pero _____ voy con _____ .
                   21.   22.

SCORE [   ]

D. Complete Lucía's questions about who's doing what after school today with **quién** or **quiénes**. (5 points)

23. ¿_____ practican el voleibol con Nelson?

24. ¿_____ va al café?

25. ¿_____ trabajan o van a la bibioteca?

26. ¿_____ quiere ir al parque conmigo?

27. ¿Con _____ habla por teléfono Margarita? ¿Habla con Lourdes?

SCORE [   ]

TOTAL SCORE [   ] /30

Spanish 1 ¡Ven conmigo!, Chapter 5

CAPÍTULO 5

El ritmo de la vida

PRIMER PASO

Maximum Score: 30

I. Listening

A. Listen as Ramón asks his friends questions about their activities. As they answer, check the appropriate column for how often each friend does that activity. (10 points)

	ACTIVITY	siempre	nunca	a veces	fines de semana
1. Luisa	desayunar				
2. Teresa	preparar la cena				
3. Alejandro	lavar los platos				
4. Juan Luis	escuchar música				
5. Enrique	trabajar en la tienda				

SCORE _____

II. Reading

B. Clara and Diego are at a dance party, and Diego doesn't know much about some of the people. Read their conversation and respond with **sí** or **no** to the statements on p. 108. (10 points)

CLARA Hola, Diego. ¿Qué tal?

DIEGO Fantástico. Me gustan mucho los bailes. Pero no conozco (*I don't know*) a nadie. ¿Quién es la chica rubia?

CLARA Es Emilia. Es muy simpática y le gusta bailar también. Ella canta muy bien también. Le gusta mucho nadar y practicar deportes. Los fines de semana va a la piscina en el parque.

DIEGO Y los chicos morenos y altos, ¿quiénes son?

CLARA Son Miguel y Gustavo. Gustavo trabaja durante la semana, pero le gusta bailar los sábados. Miguel, en cambio (*on the other hand*), no trabaja. Ayuda en casa muchas veces y siempre prepara la cena durante la semana. Y tú, Diego, ¿qué haces?

DIEGO Nunca trabajo porque no tengo tiempo. Siempre estudio durante la semana, pero los sábados lavo el carro y cuido a mi hermana antes de pasar un rato con mis amigos. También monto en bicicleta los domingos. Y tú, Clara, ¿lavas el carro o cuidas a los hermanos?

CLARA Yo cuido a mi hermana a veces, pero nunca lavo el carro. Es muy aburrido lavar el carro. Pues, tengo que irme, Diego. Adiós.

DIEGO Adiós, Clara. ¡Que te diviertas mucho! (*Have fun!*)

Quiz 5-1 B

_____ 6. A Emilia le gusta la música.

_____ 7. A Diego le gusta bailar.

_____ 8. Diego trabaja sólo cuando tiene tiempo.

_____ 9. Emilia nada los sábados y los domingos.

_____ 10. Miguel prepara la cena a veces.

_____ 11. Diego siempre hace la tarea durante la semana.

_____ 12. Clara practica un deporte todos los días.

_____ 13. Diego ayuda en casa los sábados.

_____ 14. Diego nunca practica deportes.

_____ 15. Gustavo ayuda en casa durante la semana.

SCORE [   ]

III. Writing

C. Answer each of the following questions with a sentence. Using the cues in parentheses, say how often you or others do each thing. (10 points)

16. ¿Qué haces los sábados? (always)

_____

17. ¿Con qué frecuencia desayunas? (at times)

_____

18. ¿Qué haces para ayudar en casa? (every day)

_____

19. ¿Quién toca el piano en tu casa? (no one)

_____

20. ¿Quiénes miran la televisión en tu casa? (often)

_____

SCORE [   ]

TOTAL SCORE [   ] /30

El ritmo de la vida

SEGUNDO PASO

Grammar and Vocabulary

A. Complete the statements about where people go and what activities they like to do in each place. Write the missing pronouns and then choose the most logical infinitive from the box. Use each infinitive once. (12 points)

| hacer ejercicio | recibir |
| comer esquiar leer | pescar |

1. Alonso y Beto van al lago porque _____ gusta _____ .

2. Yolanda va a la librería porque _____ gusta _____ todas las revistas nuevas.

3. Esteban y yo vamos al restaurante porque _____ gusta _____ hamburguesas.

4. ¿A ustedes _____ gusta _____ en el gimnasio nuevo, verdad?

5. Teresa y Carmen van a Colorado porque _____ gusta _____ .

6. Yo escribo muchas cartas porque _____ gusta _____ cartas también.

SCORE [   ]

B. Blanca is wondering what to get people for birthday presents. Answer her questions by telling her what each person or group likes to do. Use the infinitives given with **gusta** and the correct pronoun. Include the phrases **a él, a ella, a ellos,** or **a ellas** for clarification. (10 points)

7. ¿Qué hacen Felipe y Raúl? (correr)

_____

8. ¿Qué hace Sonia? (bucear)

_____

9. ¿Qué hacen Elena y Rafael? (asistir al teatro)

_____

10. ¿Qué hace Federico? (acampar)

_____

11. ¿Qué hacen Victoria y Ana? (jugar al tenis)

_____

SCORE [   ]

Quiz 5-2A

C. Complete the conversations about what everyone does using the correct form of the verbs in parentheses. (13 points)

—Sara, ¿tú y Linda (hacer) _____ ejercicio juntas?
                              12.

—Sí, yo (hacer) _____ ejercicio con ella todos los días. Muchas veces ella y yo
                      13.

(correr) _____ en el parque. A veces (asistir) _____ a una clase
              14.   **15.**

de ejercicios aeróbicos también.

—Álvaro, ¿qué (comer) _____ ustedes en la cafetería del colegio?
                              16.

—Yo (comer) _____ un sándwich y (beber) _____ jugo. Mi amigo
                  17.   **18.**

Chuy (comer) _____ pizza y ensaladas, y (beber) _____ agua.
                  19.   **20.**

—¿Qué (hacer) _____ Tomás en la biblioteca? ¿(Hacer) _____ la
                  21.   **22.**

tarea él y Miguel?

—No, ellos no estudian ahora. (Leer) _____ revistas y (escribir)
                                          23.

_____ cartas a sus amigos.
      24.

SCORE [   ]

TOTAL SCORE [   ] /35

Spanish 1 ¡Ven conmigo!, Chapter 5

Nombre _____ Clase _____ Fecha _____

5 El ritmo de la vida

◼ SEGUNDO PASO

Maximum Score: 35

I. Listening

A. Listen to Luz ask questions about what her friends do. Match the answers that you hear to the appropriate pictures below. (10 points)

a.   b.   c.   d.   e.

1. _____   2. _____   3. _____   4. _____   5. _____   SCORE [   ]

II. Reading

B. Look over the poll showing when classmates do different activities, then indicate if the statements that follow are **a) cierto** or **b) falso**. (10 points)

	Sara	Montse	Nando
leer las tiras cómicas	los domingos	nunca	los sábados por la mañana
ver películas	a veces	los sábados	los viernes por la noche
asistir a conciertos	nunca	los viernes	a veces
ir a la pizzería	por la tarde	los sábados	después de clases
asistir a una clase de ejercicios aeróbicos	por la mañana	por la tarde	todos los días

_____ 6. A Montse y Nando les gusta ir al cine.

_____ 7. A Sara y Montse les gusta escuchar música.

_____ 8. Sara y Nando reciben el periódico los fines de semana.

_____ 9. A todos les gusta comer pizza.

_____ 10. Los amigos nunca hacen ejercicio.   SCORE [   ]

Quiz 5-2B

III. Writing

C. Write five sentences to describe what each person or group in the illustration is doing. Use a different verb in each sentence. (10 points)

11. _____
    _____
    _____
    _____

12. _____
    _____
    _____
    _____

13. _____
    _____
    _____
    _____

14. _____
    _____
    _____
    _____

15. _____
    _____
    _____
    _____

SCORE [   ]

IV. Culture

D. Based on the information in your textbook, respond to the statements below with **a) cierto** or **b) falso**. (5 points)

_____ 16. In Spain and Latin America, most students have their own cars.

_____ 17. Students in Latin America enjoy getting together with friends in public places.

SCORE [   ]

TOTAL SCORE [   ] /35

Spanish 1 ¡Ven conmigo!, Chapter 5

CAPÍTULO 5

CAPÍTULO 5

El ritmo de la vida

QUIZ**Quiz 5-3A**

Maximum Score: 35

■ TERCER PASO

Grammar and Vocabulary

A. Write the Spanish words that correspond to the definitions. (9 points)

1. El mes antes de octubre es _____ .

2. Tres meses forman una _____ .

3. El primer mes de la primavera es _____ .

4. El mes después de julio es _____ .

5. La estación después del otoño es _____ .

6. El primer mes del año es _____ .

7. La estación antes del verano es _____ .

8. El mes después de abril es _____ .

9. Hay doce _____ en un año.

SCORE _____

CAPÍTULO 5

B. Fátima wants to know what's going to be happening in the next few weeks. Answer her questions about when events take place, writing complete sentences and using the information given. (14 points)

	October		November	
game	15th	dance	1st
test	21th	concert	5th
party	27th	dinner	22nd
trip to park	31th		

10. ¿Cuándo es el concierto? _____

11. ¿Cuándo es la fiesta? _____

12. ¿Cuándo es la excursión (*trip*) al parque? _____

13. ¿Cuándo es el examen? _____

Nombre _____ Clase _____ Fecha _____

14. ¿Cuándo es el baile? _____

15. ¿Cuándo es la cena en tu casa? _____

16. ¿Cuándo es el partido? _____

SCORE [ ]

C. Write a sentence in Spanish describing the weather in each place listed. Explain whether it's hot, cold, or cool, and what the other conditions are in each place. Use the information in the chart. (12 points)

Ciudad	Temperatura máxima	Temperatura mínima	Tiempo
Nueva York	60°	45°	
Miami	100°	85°	
Chicago	45°	40°	
San Francisco	65°	55°	
Juneau	35°	25°	
San Antonio	85°	70°	

17. _____
18. _____
19. _____
20. _____
21. _____
22. _____

SCORE [ ]

TOTAL SCORE [/35]

CAPÍTULO 5

Nombre _____ Clase _____ Fecha _____

Quiz 5-3B

■ TERCER PASO

Maximum Score: 35

I. Listening

A. Listen to descriptions of the weather for various.places. Match what you hear to the appropriate pictures below. You may use a picture more than once. (10 points)

1. _____

2. _____

3. _____

4. _____

5. _____

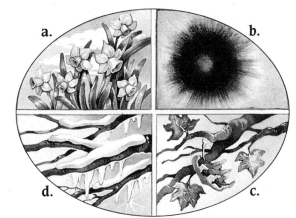

SCORE [   ]

II. Reading

B. Read the following statements about the weather, seasons, and months of the year in the Northern Hemisphere. If they are logical, write **sí**. If not, write **no**. (10 points)

_____ 6. Hace calor. Es un día maravilloso para nadar.

_____ 7. Es invierno y hace frío y nieva. Es ideal para esquiar.

_____ 8. Hoy es el primero de agosto. Nieva mucho en Miami.

_____ 9. Los meses del verano son septiembre, octubre y noviembre.

_____ 10. Hace sol y es un buen día para ir a la playa.

_____ 11. Está lloviendo. Es un día estupendo para caminar con el perro en el parque.

_____ 12. Hoy es el primer día de la primavera. Es el veintidós de diciembre.

_____ 13. En Nueva York, muchas personas van a la playa en diciembre.

_____ 14. Los meses del otoño son marzo, abril y mayo.

_____ 15. Hace frío y está nublado. Es un buen día para ver una película en casa.

SCORE [   ]

Quiz 5-3B

III. Writing

C. In a short paragraph, describe your favorite time of the year. Include your favorite season, three activities you do during that season, and a description of the weather. Begin with **Mi estación favorita es...** (11 points)

16. _____

    _____

    _____

    _____

    _____

    _____

    _____

    SCORE [   ]

IV. Culture

D. Based on the information in your textbook, respond with **a) cierto** or **b) falso** to the statements below. (4 points)

_____ 17. In the southern cone of South America, summer begins in December.

_____ 18. At the equator there are only two seasons.

SCORE [   ]

TOTAL SCORE [   ] /35

CUMULATIVE SCORE FOR QUIZZES 1–3 [   ] /100

Spanish 1 ¡Ven conmigo!, Chapter 5

CAPÍTULO 5

El ritmo de la vida

Chapter 5 Test

I. Listening

Maximum Score: 30 points

A. Listen as Tomás tells you about the pictures below. Write the letter of the picture he describes. (15 points)

a.

b.

c.

d.

e.

1. _____

2. _____

3. _____

4. _____

5. _____

SCORE _____

CAPÍTULO 5

B. Beatriz and Memo are talking about things they like to do and how often they do them. Listen to their comments and decide what they do and don't have in common. Then, complete these statements about the two of them. (15 points)

6. A Beatriz le gusta ir a los restaurantes con sus amigos _____ a la semana.
   a. una vez   **b.** dos o tres veces

7. Memo necesita ir al parque _____.
   a. los sábados   **b.** todos los días

8. La actividad favorita de Memo es _____.
   a. esquiar   **b.** correr

9. Los amigos van a ir a Colorado para las vacaciones de _____.
   a. primavera   **b.** verano

10. A Memo le gusta mucho la nieve especialmente cuando _____.
    a. no hace mucho frío   **b.** hace sol y frío al mismo tiempo

SCORE _____

Chapter 5 Test

II. Reading

C. Read what Julia has to say about what she and her friends think of spring and summer. Then indicate if the statements that follow are correct with **a) sí** or **b) no**. (12 points)

> ¡Qué buen tiempo hace en la primavera! A mis amigas y a mí nos gusta mucho esta estación. No nieva ni *(nor)* hace frío. Llueve a veces pero no hace calor—siempre hace fresco. Corremos por la playa todos los días, acampamos los fines de semana y pescamos muchas veces también. ¿Quién quiere asistir a clases o ayudar en casa cuando hace tan *(such)* buen tiempo? ¡Nadie! A todos les gusta pasar el rato con sus amigos al aire libre *(outdoors)*. Cuando llega el verano nadie quiere hacer nada. Mis amigas y yo nos quedamos *(stay)* en casa. Miramos la televisión, les escribimos cartas a nuestros amigos y leemos tiras cómicas. Nos gusta el verano sólo cuando nadamos en la piscina en el parque. A nosotras nos gusta más la primavera, especialmente durante los días de vacaciones.

_____ **11.** In the spring, Julia and her friends prefer outdoor activities to indoor activities.

_____ **12.** Julia likes going to school in the spring.

_____ **13.** Julia likes to swim but her friends don't.

_____ **14.** Julia and her friends like spring better than summer.

SCORE [   ]

CAPÍTULO 5

D. José has filled out a questionnaire about diet and exercise. Look over the questionnaire, then indicate if José made the statements that follow by writing **a) sí** or **b) no**, based on what you read. (18 points)

- ¿A usted le gusta comer hamburguesas y papas fritas?
  Nunca como hamburguesas. No me gustan. Me gusta comer ensaladas y fruta.

- ¿Siempre desayuna usted?
  Desayuno sólo los fines de semana. No tengo tiempo de desayunar durante la semana.

- ¿Asiste usted a clases de ejercicios aeróbicos?
  No me gustan los aeróbicos. Pero corro dos millas por la mañana todos los días.

- ¿Bebe usted mucha agua?
  Sí. Bebo ocho vasos (glasses) de agua todos los días.

- ¿Hace usted ejercicio en el verano?
  Cuando hace calor nunca hago ejercicio. En el verano voy a la piscina o leo el periódico en el parque.

_____ 15. ¡Hace mucho sol! ¿Vamos a nadar por la tarde hoy?

_____ 16. Siempre compro una hamburguesa en la cafetería para el almuerzo.

_____ 17. La clase de matemáticas es a las ocho. Por eso, siempre desayuno a las siete y media.

_____ 18. Me gusta mucho ir al gimnasio porque las clases de aeróbicos allí son excelentes.

_____ 19. No me gusta correr por la tarde. Corro por la mañana porque hace fresco entonces.

_____ 20. ¡Qué calor hace! Quiero beber un vaso de agua muy grande.

SCORE [ ]

CAPÍTULO 5

III. Culture

Maximum Score: 9 points

E. Based on the information in your textbook, decide whether the following statements are **a) cierto** or **b) falso**. (9 points)

_____ 21. Spanish-speaking teenagers often have weekday routines similar to those of teenagers in the United States.

_____ 22. Spending time with groups of friends is unimportant in the lives of Spanish-speaking teens.

_____ 23. Even though it is near the equator, the Andes region is cold because of its altitude.

SCORE [ ]

Chapter 5 Test

IV. Writing

F. Based on the following pictures, write a sentence in Spanish to describe the weather on a particular day. Include the date and season in each sentence. (8 points)

24. _____

_____

25. _____

_____

26. _____

_____

27. _____

_____

SCORE _____

G. Answer the questions below in complete sentences in Spanish. (14 points)

28. ¿Cuál es la fecha?

   _____

   _____

29. ¿Qué tiempo hace hoy?

   _____

   _____

30. ¿Cuáles son los meses del verano en los Estados Unidos?

   _____

   _____

31. ¿Cuándo hace frío en Miami?

   _____

   _____

32. ¿Qué les gusta hacer a ti y a tus amigos cuando hace calor?

   _____

   _____

33. ¿Con qué frecuencia escribes cartas en el invierno?

   _____

   _____

34. Típicamente, ¿hace más fresco por la mañana, por la tarde o por la noche?

   _____

   _____

SCORE [   ]

CAPÍTULO 5

Chapter 5 Test

H. Write three sentences in Spanish telling what you like to do in at least three different seasons or weather situations. Include where, how often, and who you do the activities with. (9 points)

35. _____

_____

36. _____

_____

37. _____

_____

SCORE [   ]

TOTAL SCORE [/100]

CAPÍTULO 5

CAPÍTULO 5 Chapter Test Score Sheet

Circle the letter that matches the most appropriate response.

I. Listening
Maximum Score: 30 points

A. (15 points)

1. a b c d e
2. a b c d e
3. a b c d e
4. a b c d e
5. a b c d e

SCORE _____

B. (15 points)

6. a b
7. a b
8. a b
9. a b
10. a b

SCORE _____

II. Reading
Maximum Score: 30 points

C. (12 points)

11. a b
12. a b
13. a b
14. a b

SCORE _____

D. (18 points)

15. a b
16. a b
17. a b
18. a b
19. a b
20. a b

SCORE _____

III. Culture
Maximum Score: 9 points

E. (9 points)

21. a b
22. a b
23. a b

SCORE _____

CAPÍTULO 5

IV. Writing

CAPÍTULO 5

F. (8 points)

24. _____

_____

25. _____

_____

26. _____

_____

27. _____

_____

SCORE [   ]

G. (14 points)

28. _____
29. _____
30. _____
31. _____
32. _____
33. _____
34. _____

SCORE [   ]

H. (9 points)

35. _____

_____

36. _____

_____

37. _____

_____

SCORE [   ]

TOTAL SCORE [   ] /100

Spanish 1 ¡Ven conmigo!, Chapter 5

Scripts for Quizzes 5-1B, 5-2B, 5-3B

Quiz 5-1B Capítulo 5 Primer paso

I. Listening
A. 1. RAMÓN   Oye, Luisa, ¿con qué frecuencia desayunas?
        LUISA   ¿Yo? Siempre. Me gusta mucho la comida.
    2. RAMÓN   Y tú, Teresa, ¿siempre preparas la cena?
        TERESA No, pero los fines de semana preparo la cena en casa.
    3. RAMÓN   Alejandro, ¿lavas los platos en casa?
        ALEJANDRO Sí, a veces, pero no es divertido.
    4. RAMÓN   Y Juan Luis, ¿con qué frecuencia escuchas música?
        JUAN LUIS Pues, en realidad, no me gusta; nunca escucho música.
    5. RAMÓN   Enrique ¿todavía trabajas en la tienda los domingos?
        ENRIQUE Sí, y los sábados también.

Quiz 5-2B Capítulo 5 Segundo paso

I. Listening
A. 1. LUZ   ¿Beben ustedes jugo de naranja, Mario y Alejandro?
        MARIO   Sí, nos gusta mucho el jugo de naranja.
    2. LUZ   ¿Dónde les gusta hacer ejercicio a Mari y Chela?
        LUISA   En el gimnasio.
    3. LUZ   ¿Qué hace Susana?
        ADRIANA Ella bucea en el lago.
    4. LUZ   ¿Qué hacen las chicas?
        MARCO   Corren cinco millas por la playa.
    5. LUZ   ¿Les gusta a ustedes comer un sándwich o una ensalada para el almuerzo?
        JUAN   Nos gusta comer un sándwich y beber leche.

Quiz 5-3B Capítulo 5 Tercer paso

I. Listening
A. 1. Hoy es el primero de enero en Nueva York. Hace mucho frío hoy.
    2. Hace mucho sol en Miami porque estamos en pleno verano.
    3. En Chicago es la primavera y hace mucho fresco.
    4. Es un día perfecto para esquiar aquí en Colorado. Hace mucho frío y nieva.
    5. Es otoño y hace fresco en Boston.

Answers to Quizzes 5-1A, 5-1B

ANSWERS Quiz 5-1A

A. (8 points: 1 point per item)
Some answers may vary. Possible
answers:
1. durante la semana/todos los días
2. con qué frecuencia
3. todos los días/siempre
4. siempre/todos los días
5. muchas veces/a veces
6. a veces/muchas veces
7. sólo cuando
8. todavía

B. (9 points: 1.5 points per item)
9. No quiere comprar nada para su
cuarto.
10. Nunca estudia/No estudia nunca los
fines de semana.
11. Nadie va con ella/Ella no va con
nadie al centro comercial.
12. No necesita comprar nada para las
clases.
13. Nunca cuida/No cuida nunca a su
hermanito.
14. Nadie camina con ella en el parque.

C. (8 points: 1 point per item)
15. No
16. nada
17. nunca
18. nunca
19. nadie
20. Nunca
21. no
22. nadie

D. (5 points: 1 point per item)
23. Quiénes
24. Quién
25. Quiénes
26. Quién
27. quién

ANSWERS Quiz 5-1B

I. Listening

A. (10 points: 2 points per item)
1. siempre
2. los fines de semana
3. a veces
4. nunca
5. los fines de semana

II. Reading

B. (10 points: 1 point per item)
6. sí
7. sí
8. no
9. sí
10. sí
11. sí
12. no
13. sí
14. no
15. no

III. Writing

C. (10 points: 2 points per item)
Answers will vary. Possible answers:
16. Siempre ayudo a mi mamá. Lavo la
ropa.
17. A veces desayuno durante la semana: los lunes, los miércoles y los
viernes.
18. Todos los días preparo la cena, cuido a mi hermanito/a y saco la
basura.
19. Nadie toca el piano en mi casa.
20. Mis hermanos miran la televisión
muchas veces por la tarde.

ANSWERS Quiz 5-2A

A. (12 points: 1 point per item)
1. les, pescar/esquiar
2. le, leer
3. nos, comer
4. les, hacer ejercicio
5. les, esquiar
6. me, recibir

B. (10 points: 2 points per item)
7. A ellos les gusta correr.
8. A ella le gusta bucear.
9. A ellos les gusta asistir al teatro.
10. A él le gusta acampar.
11. A ellas les gusta jugar al tenis.

C. (13 points: 1 point per item)
12. hacen
13. hago
14. corremos
15. asistimos
16. comen
17. como
18. bebo
19. come
20. bebe
21. hace
22. Hacen
23. Leen
24. escriben

ANSWERS Quiz 5-2B

I. Listening

A. (10 points: 2 points per item)
1. e   2. c   3. d   4. a   5. b

II. Reading

B. (10 points: 2 points per item)
6. a
7. b
8. a
9. a
10. b

III. Writing

C. (10 points: 2 points per item)
Answers will vary. Possible answers:
11. Los Gómez caminan.
12. Ricardo y Julia corren.
13. Adriana come un sándwich.
14. Sandra come una hamburguesa.
15. María y Juan pescan.

IV. Culture

D. (5 points: 2.5 points per item)
16. b
17. a

CAPITULO 5

Answers to Quizzes 5-3A, 5-3B

ANSWERS Quiz 5-3A

A. (9 points: 1 point per item)
1. septiembre
2. estación
3. marzo
4. agosto
5. invierno
6. enero
7. primavera
8. mayo
9. meses

B. (14 points: 2 points per item)
10. El concierto es el cinco de noviembre.
11. La fiesta es el veintisiete de octubre.
12. La excursión al parque es el treinta y uno de octubre.
13. El examen es el veintiuno de octubre.
14. El baile es el primero de noviembre.
15. La cena en mi casa es el veintidós de noviembre.
16. El partido es el quince de octubre.

C. (12 points: 2 points per item)
Some answers will vary. Possible answers:
17. En Nueva York, hace fresco y está nublado.
18. En Miami, hace mucho calor y hace sol.
19. En Chicago, hace frío y hace viento.
20. En San Francisco, hace fresco y está lloviendo.
21. En Juneau, hace mucho frío y está nevando.
22. En San Antonio, hace calor y está lloviendo.

ANSWERS Quiz 5-3B

I. Listening

A. (10 points: 2 points per item)
1. d 2. b 3. a 4. d 5. c

II. Reading

B. (10 points: 1 point per item)
6. sí
7. sí
8. no
9. no
10. sí
11. no
12. no
13. no
14. no
15. sí

III. Writing

C. (11 points)
Answers will vary. Possible answer:
16. Mi estación favorita es el otoño porque hace fresco y no hace mucho calor. No llueve ni nieva. Corro en el parque todos los días en el otoño. A veces me gusta acampar y pescar con mi amigo.

IV. Culture

D. (4 points: 2 points per item)
17. a   18. a

Scripts for Chapter 5 Test

I. Listening

A.
1. En el invierno la chica esquía en Colorado.
2. Luis siempre nada cuando hace calor.
3. A veces Raquel y Armando almuerzan en la cafetería.
4. Los chicos corren en el parque en la primavera.
5. A Juanita le gusta escribir cartas en la biblioteca.

B.

BEATRIZ	A mí me gusta mucho conocer gente nueva. Por eso me gusta ir a los restaurantes con mis amigos dos o tres veces a la semana.
MEMO	¡Sí, ya sé, Beatriz! Tú puedes pasar toda la semana en conversaciones con tus amigos. A mí eso no me gusta para nada. Necesito hacer muchas cosas. Yo necesito ir al parque a correr todos los días... ¡Pero esquiar es mi actividad favorita!
BEATRIZ	Entonces, ¿por qué no vienes a Colorado con nosotros el cinco de marzo? Estamos planeando ir allá con Silvia y Fernando para las vacaciones de primavera.
MEMO	¡Perfecto! Me gusta mucho la nieve... especialmente cuando hace sol y frío al mismo tiempo.

Answers to Chapter 5 Test

I. Listening Maximum Score: 30 points

A. (15 points: 3 points per item)
1. c
2. a
3. e
4. d
5. b

B. (15 points: 3 points per item)
6. b
7. b
8. a
9. a
10. b

II. Reading Maximum Score: 30 points

C. (12 points: 3 points per item)
11. a
12. b
13. b
14. a

D. (18 points: 3 points per item)
15. a
16. b
17. b
18. b
19. a
20. a

III. Culture Maximum Score: 9 points

E. (9 points: 3 points per item)
21. a
22. b
23. a

IV. Writing Maximum Score: 31 points

F. (8 points: 2 points per item)
Answers will vary. Possible answers:
24. Hoy es el primero de febrero. Es invierno y hace mucho frío.
25. Hoy es el cuatro de julio. Es verano y hace calor y sol.
26. Hoy es el ocho de enero. Es invierno y nieva mucho.
27. Hoy es el diez de marzo. Es primavera y hace mucho viento y llueve.

G. (14 points: 2 points per item)
Answers will vary. Possible answers:
28. Hoy es el (*current date*).
29. Hoy hace (calor, fresco...).
30. Los meses del verano son junio, julio y agosto.
31. Hace frío en Miami en enero.
32. Cuando hace calor, nos gusta (nadar, esquiar en el agua...).
33. Casi nunca escribo cartas en el invierno.
34. Hace más fresco por la noche.

H. (9 points: 3 points per item)
Answers will vary. Possible answers:
35. Durante la primavera me gusta correr en el parque a veces con mi hermano.
36. En el invierno me gusta esquiar en las montañas con mis amigos durante los fines de semana.
37. Durante el otoño me gusta ir a fiestas todos los fines de semana con mis amigos.

CAPÍTULO **6** Entre familia

Quiz 6-1A

PRIMER PASO

Maximum Score: 35

Grammar and Vocabulary

A. Look at the Chávez family tree, then complete the statements with the missing words. (10 points)

1. Clara es la _____ de Fabiola.

2. La _____ de Pedro es María.

3. Luis y Pascual son _____ .

4. Fernanda es la _____ de Luis.

5. Geraldo es el _____ de Fabiola.

6. Pasqual es el _____ de Fernanda.

7. María es la _____ de Geraldo.

8. Diego es el _____ de Elisa.

9. Elisa es la _____ de Luis.

10. La _____ de María es Clara.

Diego   Clara

Geraldo   María   Fernanda

Pedro

Luis   Fabiola   Pascual   Elisa

SCORE [ ]

B. Look over the family tree again, then read what different family members say about one another. Put a check mark next to the person most likely to have made each statement. (9 points)

11. Mi hijo sólo tiene 12 años, pero es muy alto. Es moreno, como su tío.
_____ Pedro
_____ Diego
_____ Geraldo

12. No me gusta mi prima Fabiola. Es muy antipática.
_____ María
_____ Elisa
_____ Luis

13. Mis hijos y mi esposa son morenos, pero soy rubio.
_____ Geraldo
_____ Clara
_____ Fernanda

14. Qué similares son mi esposa y mi hija, ¿verdad? Las dos son altas y rubias.
_____ Diego
_____ Pedro
_____ Geraldo

15. Me gusta visitar a mis abuelos. Abuelo es estricto pero simpático.
_____ Pasqual
_____ Fernanda
_____ Clara

16. ¡Qué buena es la hija de mi hijo Pedro! Estudia mucho y es muy inteligente.
_____ Clara
_____ Fernanda
_____ María.

SCORE [ ]

CAPÍTULO 6

C. Ricky is writing a description of his family for Spanish class and needs your help. Complete these sentences with the missing Spanish words. (16 points)

17. Mis hermanos y yo vivimos con _____ .
(*our mother*)

18. _____ están divorciados.
(*My parents*)

19. _____ se llaman Archy y Betina.
(*Our dogs*)

20. Teresa, la nueva esposa de mi papá, es _____ .
(*my stepmother*)

21. _____ son Daniel y Greg.
(*Her children*)

22. Ellos son _____ .
(*my stepbrothers*)

23. _____ vive en Chicago.
(*Their father*)

24. _____ viven en Chicago también.
(*Their cousins*)

SCORE ____

TOTAL SCORE ____ /35

Spanish 1 ¡Ven conmigo!, Chapter 6

CAPITULO 6

CAPÍTULO

6 Entre familia

■ PRIMER PASO

I. Listening

A. First locate Carlos in the family tree below. Then study the illustration, and answer **sí** or **no** to indicate whether his statements are accurate or not. (10 points)

1. _____
2. _____
3. _____
4. _____
5. _____

SCORE [   ]

II. Reading

B. Antonio is with María at a family party. He doesn't know many of her relatives. Read their conversation and then respond with **sí** or **no** to the statements that follow. (8 points)

ANTONIO ¿Cuántas personas hay en tu familia?
MARÍA Hay muchas. Nuestra familia es grande.
ANTONIO ¿Quién es el chico alto?
MARÍA Es mi hermano José.
ANTONIO ¿Y la chica rubia y bonita que está a su lado?
MARÍA Es mi prima Inés. Es muy simpática. Ella tiene tres hermanos: Juan, Isabel y Bárbara. Isabel y Bárbara son muy cómicas e inteligentes también.
ANTONIO ¿Y el señor moreno y alto? ¿Es tu padre?
MARÍA No, es Gregorio, mi padrastro. Es muy simpático.
ANTONIO ¿Y la chica baja y rubia?
MARÍA Es Clara, la hija de Gregorio. Es mi hermanastra.

_____ 6. El hermano de María es alto.

_____ 7. Inés y Bárbara son primas.

_____ 8. Gregorio es el esposo de la mamá de María.

_____ 9. Clara es la hermanastra de José.

SCORE [   ]

CAPÍTULO 6

Quiz 6-1 B

III. Writing

C. Identify and describe each member of this family. Write two sentences for each person. Include ages, likes and dislikes, pastimes, appearance, and personality. (12 points)

10. _____

_____

11. _____

_____

12. _____

_____

SCORE [   ]

IV. Culture

D. Based on the information in your textbook, respond with **a) cierto** or **b) falso** to the following statements. (5 points)

_____ 13. People in Spanish-speaking countries tend to spend more time with friends and family than do people in the United States.

_____ 14. Godparents are expected to give advice, affection, and even help with school-related expenses.

SCORE [   ]

TOTAL SCORE [   ] /35

CAPÍTULO 6

6 Entre familia

Nombre _____ Clase _____ Fecha _____

■ SEGUNDO PASO

Maximum Score: 35

Grammar and Vocabulary

A. Adrián and Miguel are talking about their families. Complete their conversation with the words and expressions from the box. Use each expression only once. (12 points)

viejos	travieso	menor	De qué color es	canas	pelirrojo
ojos		se ve	mayor	atractiva	cómo son	listos

ADRIÁN   Miguel, ¿_____ tus hermanos?
1.

MIGUEL   Son muy _____ . Beni, mi hermano _____ , tiene 17 años. Ricardo,
2.   3.

mi hermano _____ , tiene 10 años. Es muy _____ .
4.   5.

ADRIÁN   ¿Ellos son rubios, como tú? ¿_____ el pelo de Beni?
6.

MIGUEL   Beni es _____ , como mi mamá. Pero Ricardo sí es rubio, como yo. Y los dos
7.

tienen _____ verdes.
8.

ADRIÁN   ¿Y cuántos años tienen tus abuelos? ¿Son muy _____ ?
9.

MIGUEL   Pues, mi abuelo tiene 68 años. Él tiene _____ y es un poco gordo. Y mi abuela
10.

tiene 60 años. Ella todavía _____ joven. Es una mujer muy _____ .
11.   12.

SCORE [   ]

B. There are a lot of similarities between different members of the Montoya family. Complete the statements about how different relatives resemble one another with the correct form of the adjectives. (8 points)

13. La tía Juliana es pelirroja, y sus hijos son _____ también.

14. Abuelo es un poco gordo, y su hija Liliana también es un poco _____ .

15. ¡Qué travieso es Benjamín! Sus hermanas también son muy _____ .

16. Miguel es muy alto y delgado, porque sus padres son _____ y _____ .

Quiz 6-2A

17. Abuela tiene 70 años, pero es una mujer muy atractiva. Sus hermanas también son muy

_____ .

18. Abuelo se ve muy joven, ¿verdad? Y los tíos también se ven muy _____ para su edad.

19. Tania es muy lista, y sus tres hermanos son _____ también. Es una familia muy

inteligente.

SCORE [ ]

C. Complete Norma's description of what she and her family do on weekends with the correct form of **hacer** or **salir**. (9 points)

¿Qué _____ mi familia y yo los fines de semana? Pues, los sábados, ayudo mucho en
          20.

casa. Por la mañana siempre _____ las camas. Pero mi hermano nunca _____
                    21.   **22.**

nada. ¡Él es muy perezoso! El sábado por la noche, todos nosotros _____ juntos para
                                      23.

cenar en mi restaurante favorito. El domingo, yo _____ con mis amigas. Muchas veces
                          24.

vamos al parque. Mis padres también _____ Van a la casa de mis tíos.
                        25.

SCORE [ ]

D. Read the statements about what the Padilla family is doing this weekend, and complete each one with the personal **a** if necessary. If it's not necessary, mark an X in the blank. (6 points)

26. Nuria y Carlos van al cine para ver _____ la película nueva.

27. El señor Padilla necesita ir al hospital para visitar _____ un amigo que está allí.

28. La señora Padilla quiere ir al centro y mirar _____ unas tiendas.

29. A Suso le gusta el arte. Quiere ver _____ el nuevo museo de arte.

30. Lourdes va a una fiesta en casa de su amiga Ana. Quiere conocer _____ toda su

familia.

31. Abuela quiere ir al parque y ver _____ todas las personas que están allí.

SCORE [ ]

TOTAL SCORE [/35]

Spanish 1 ¡Ven conmigo!, Chapter 6

CAPÍTULO

6 Entre familia

■ SEGUNDO PASO

I. Listening

A. Pedro is describing several photos that he has found. Listen to his descriptions and see if you can match each photo with what he says. (10 points)

a.

b.

c.

d.

e.

1. _____ 2. _____ 3. _____ 4. _____ 5. _____

SCORE [ ]

II. Reading

B. Read each of the following descriptions below and decide which picture it best matches. More than one description may match each photo. (10 points)

a.

b.

c.

_____ 6. Quiero mucho a mis hijas, pero Susana es un poco traviesa.

_____ 7. A veces salgo con mi mamá y mi hermana mayor a cenar en un restaurante mexicano. ¡Qué divertido!

Quiz 6-2B

_____ 8. Mi papá y yo casi siempre visitamos a mi abuelita los fines de semana. Ella es muy cariñosa. Tiene canas y los ojos de color café.

_____ 9. Mi papá es un poco gordo. ¿Y mi hermana mayor Sara? Pues, ella es muy inteligente y lista. Mañana hacemos una fiesta para celebrar su graduación del colegio.

_____ 10. Tengo 69 años, pero nunca estoy aburrida porque mi hijo y mi nieto me visitan casi todos los fines de semana. Y durante el verano siempre hacemos un viaje juntos.

SCORE [   ]

III. Writing

C. You're planning to stay with a family in Guatemala next summer. Let them know your plans by writing a sentence in Spanish for each of the following pieces of information. (12 points)

11. You're leaving New York on June 15.

_____

12. You are short, dark, and thin.

_____

13. You want to visit your friend Rodolfo when you're in Guatemala.

_____

14. You also want to visit some ruins (*ruinas*).

_____

SCORE [   ]

IV. Culture

D. Based on the information in your textbook, respond with **a) cierto** or **b) falso** to the statements below. (3 points)

_____ 15. Spanish speakers often share their problems with other family members rather than dealing with them alone.

_____ 16. In Spanish-speaking families, the desire to be alone for long periods might be interpreted as a sign of a problem.

_____ 17. Teenagers in Spain and Latin America rarely help out around the house.

SCORE [   ]

TOTAL SCORE [   ] /35

Spanish 1 ¡Ven conmigo!, Chapter 6

CAPITULO 6

CAPÍTULO

6

Entre familia

■ TERCER PASO

Grammar and Vocabulary

A. Señor Moreno has some ideas about what his family should do. Complete what he says to his wife Teresa with the correct form of **deber**. (8 points)

Teresa, estoy un poco gordo. _____ ir al gimnasio para hacer ejercicio, todos los
                                        1.

días. Y tú, mi amor, trabajas demasiado. _____ descansar más. Tengo una idea.
                                                    2.

Todos nosotros _____ ayudar más en casa con los quehaceres. Beto y Fede
                        3.

_____ sacar la basura todas las noches. Y Clara _____ ayudar a preparar la
        4.   5.

cena. Todos nuestros hijos _____ organizar sus cuartos. Yo _____ lavar los
                                    6.   7.

platos después de cenar. Y tú y yo _____ caminar con el perro después de cenar.
                                            8.

SCORE _____

B. There is a lot of work to be done at Lalo's house. Complete the statements about what everyone should do with the correct form of **deber** and the missing infinitives from the box. (16 points)

planchar	pasar	cortar	hacer
limpiar	trabajar	cuidar	poner

9. Pablo _____ _____ el césped.

10. Diana, tú y yo _____ _____ las camas, ¿no?

11. Y después, yo _____ _____ la cocina.

12. ¡La sala es un desastre! Marisa _____ _____ la aspiradora ahora mismo.

13. ¿Y quiénes _____ _____ la mesa?

14. Susanita no debe estar sola (*alone*). David _____ _____ a ella.

15. No hay ropa limpia en mi armario. _____ _____ ropa ahora.

16. ¡Qué feo está el patio! Nosotros _____ _____ en el jardín por la tarde, ¿verdad?

SCORE _____

Quiz 6-3A

C. Eduardo's family just found out that Aunt Enriqueta is coming over for a surprise visit. Complete what Eduardo says about getting the house cleaned up with the correct form of **poner**. (6 points)

17. Mamá _____ la ropa en el armario.

18. Yo _____ todas mis libros y revistas en el escritorio.

19. Papá y Esteban _____ la mesa.

20. Silvia _____ su mochila en su cuarto.

21. Mamá, ¿dónde _____ nosotros la aspiradora? ¿Debajo de la cama?

22. Roberto necesita _____ sus zapatillas en su cuarto.

SCORE [＿＿＿]

TOTAL SCORE [＿＿＿] /30

CAPÍTULO 6

Entre familia

■ TERCER PASO

Maximum Score: 30

I. Listening

A. María Elena is describing the chores that her family must do to keep the house neat and clean. Based on María Elena's description, put items **a** to **e** in the order they happen. (10 points)

a.   b.   c.   d.   e.

1. _____ 2. _____ 3. _____ 4. _____ 5. _____

SCORE _____

II. Reading

B. Read the following letter from an advice column. Then indicate with **sí** or **no** whether the letter writer should take the advice that follows. (8 points)

> Querida Ana,
> Tengo un problema. Mi mamá dice que no ayudo lo suficiente en casa. Dice que siempre miro mucha televisión. Pero no es cierto. Mi mamá no comprende. Cuando regreso del colegio todos los días, quiero descansar un poco. Mis clases este semestre son difíciles y siempre tengo mucha tarea. No es posible hacer la tarea y ayudar a mi mamá. ¿Qué debo hacer?
> Un buen estudiante con problemas en casa

"Buen estudiante"...

_____ **6.** debe hablar con su mamá y explicarle (*explain*) la situación.

_____ **7.** debe salir con sus amigos después de clases porque la tarea no es importante.

Quiz 6-3B

_____ **8.** debe ayudar a su mamá los fines de semana cuando no tiene tarea.

_____ **9.** no debe ayudar a su mamá ni hacer la tarea.

SCORE [   ]

III. Writing

C. Rogelio is taking care of his younger brothers and sisters today. One of his brothers is asking who should do which household chores. Using the cues in parentheses, write Rogelio's answers in Spanish. (12 points)

10. The cat needs attention. Who should look after it? (You should . . .)

_____

11. The living room is a mess. Should Marta or Ramón clean it? (She should . . .)

_____

12. Everyone is ready to eat. Shouldn't you and I set the table? (We should . . .)

_____

13. Maribel and Rubén are just goofing around. Shouldn't they clean the kitchen? (They should . . .)

_____

14. The grass is really tall. Who should cut it? (I should . . .)

_____

15. The clothes you just washed are all wrinkled. Should Marisol and I iron them? (You (both) should . . .)

_____

SCORE [   ]

TOTAL SCORE [   ] /30

CUMULATIVE SCORE FOR QUIZZES 1–3 [   ] /100

Spanish 1 ¡Ven conmigo!, Chapter 6

Entre familia

I. Listening

Maximum Score: 30 points

A. Look carefully at Ana's family tree and listen as she introduces her family to you. Match the correct name to each family member she introduces. (15 points)

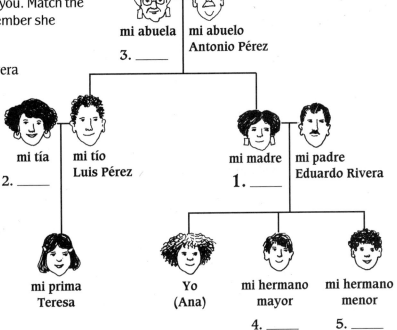

a. Olga Pérez Gómez de Rivera
b. Eduardo Rivera Pérez
c. Jorge Rivera Pérez
d. Elsa Acosta de Pérez
e. Luisa Gómez de Pérez

mi abuela | mi abuelo
Antonio Pérez

3. _____

mi tía   mi tío
Luis Pérez

2. _____

mi madre | mi padre
Eduardo Rivera

1. _____

mi prima
Teresa

Yo
(Ana)

mi hermano
mayor

mi hermano
menor

4. _____   5. _____

SCORE [   ]

B. Listen to a few short dialogues at the Pérez house. Decide which picture goes with each dialogue. Then decide if the statement in item 10 is **a) true** or **b) false**. (15 points)

a.

b.

c.

d.

6. _____   7. _____   8. _____   9. _____

10. _____   The children complain a lot about doing chores.

SCORE [   ]

C A P Í T U L O 6

Spanish 1 ¡Ven conmigo!, Chapter 6

Testing Program **143**

Chapter 6 Test

II. Reading

C. Read the description that José gives about his extended family. Write the letter of the phrase that best completes his description. (15 points)

Nuestra familia es bastante grande y muy divertida. Tengo dos hermanas y dos hermanos. Mi mamá se llama Rebeca y tiene dos hermanos, mi tía Alicia y mi tío Arturo.

_____ 11. Tía Alicia...
   a. es la tía de Rafael
   b. tiene treinta años
   c. es la hermana de Rebeca

Tía Alicia es alta y pelirroja y muy simpática. Ella es profesora de español en un colegio. Su hijo, Rafael, tiene dieciocho años y es estudiante. Su hija, mi prima Rosita, tiene doce años y es muy traviesa.

_____ 12. Rosita es...
   a. la hermana de Rafael
   b. la mamá de José
   c. la hija de Arturo

Tío Arturo y Tía Luisa viven en Santiago y tienen tres hijas que se llaman Marta, Sara y Susana. Marta tiene catorce años. Es un poco gorda y muy simpática.

_____ 13. Tío Arturo es...
   a. el hermano de José
   b. primo de Rafael
   c. el esposo de Luisa

Sara tiene trece años. Susana, la hija menor, tiene sólo tres años. Mis abuelos, Elsa y Manuel, viven muy cerca de aquí. Nos gusta salir con ellos y con nuestros tíos y primos.

_____ 14. Elsa es...
   a. la mamá de Pilar
   b. la tía de José
   c. la abuela de José

Papá se llama Rogelio y mis padres tienen otros cuatro hijos—dos hijos y dos hijas. Mis hermanas son Pilar y Juanita. Tomás y Julio son mis hermanos. ¡Qué buena familia!

_____ 15. Tomás es...
   a. el papá de Rosita
   b. el hermano de José
   c. el abuelo de Rebeca

SCORE [ ]

CAPÍTULO 6

D. There are several announcements for lost pets at the veterinarian's office. Read the anounce-ments and the statements that follow. Then write the letter of the pet described by each statement. (15 points)

> ¿Dónde está mi gata?
> Mi gata se llama Nica. Es blanca y negra y tiene ojos verdes. Es muy pequeña, delgada y lista.
> Llamar al 341-8053.

2 perros perdidos (*lost*) en el parque
Mis perros se llaman Dolfo y Bito. Dolfo
es viejo y un poco gordo. Tiene pelo
negro con canas y ojos negros. Bito
tiene pelo blanco, un ojo azul y uno de
color café. Es joven y travieso.
Llamar al 549-4335.

> Quiero encontrar a mi gato
> Mi gato se llama Ernie. Tiene ojos de color café y pelo negro. Es muy gordo. No es muy listo, pero es cariñoso.
>
> Llamar al 388-1486.

a. Nica   **b.** Dolfo   **c.** Bito   **d.** Ernie

_____ **16.** This pet is a little overweight.

_____ **17.** This pet is affectionate.

_____ **18.** This pet has green eyes.

_____ **19.** This pet isn't very smart.

_____ **20.** This pet is has two different-colored eyes.

SCORE [   ]

CAPÍTULO 6

Chapter 6 Test

III. Culture

Maximum Score: 12 points

E. Read the statements below. Based on the information in your textbook, determine whether the statements are **a) cierto** or **b) falso**. (6 points)

_____ 21. In Spanish-speaking countries, families are often large and close-knit.

_____ 22. Family members in Spanish-speaking countries rarely spend time together or depend on each other for support.

SCORE [   ]

F. Explain two roles and responsibilities of godparents in Hispanic culture. (6 points)

23. _____

_____

24. _____

_____

SCORE [   ]

Nombre _____ Clase _____ Fecha _____

IV. Writing

Maximum Score: 28 points

G. Imagine you're a member of the Gómez family. You are showing this portrait of your family to a friend. Choose five people and write two sentences to introduce and describe each of them. Each sentence should include one possessive adjective and two physical descriptions. (15 points)

25. _____

_____

26. _____

_____

27. _____

_____

28. _____

_____

29. _____

_____

SCORE [   ]

C A P Í T U L O 6

Chapter 6 Test

H. It was your job to clean the house today, but you didn't have time. You left a lot of chores to be done. Your younger brother agreed to help you out, but he needs to know what to do. Based on the picture, write a note telling your brother what he ought to do to help you. Your note should include at least three sentences and at least five things your brother should do. (13 points)

30. _____

_____

_____

_____

_____

_____

_____

_____

_____

SCORE [   ]

TOTAL SCORE [   ] /100

Spanish 1 ¡Ven conmigo!, Chapter 6

CAPÍTULO 6 Chapter Test Score Sheet

Circle the letter that matches the most appropriate response.

I. Listening   Maximum Score: 30 points

A. (15 points)   **B.** (15 points)

  1. a b c d e   6. a b c d e

  2. a b c d e   7. a b c d e

  3. a b c d e   8. a b c d e

  4. a b c d e   9. a b c d e

  5. a b c d e   10. a b

SCORE [   ]   SCORE [   ]

II. Reading   Maximum Score: 30 points

C. (15 points)   **D.** (15 points)

 11. a b c d   16. a b c d

 12. a b c d   17. a b c d

 13. a b c d   18. a b c d

 14. a b c d   19. a b c d

 15. a b c d   20. a b c d

SCORE [   ]   SCORE [   ]

III. Culture   Maximum Score: 12 points

E. (6 points)   **F.** (6 points)

 21. a b   23. _____

 22. a b   _____

                             24. _____

                                 _____

SCORE [   ]   SCORE [   ]

CAPÍTULO 6

IV. Writing

Maximum Score: 28 points

G. (15 points)

25. _____
_____

26. _____
_____

27. _____
_____

28. _____
_____

29. _____
_____

SCORE [ ]

H. (13 points)

30. _____
_____
_____
_____
_____
_____
_____
_____
_____

SCORE [ ]

TOTAL SCORE [ ] /100

Spanish 1 ¡Ven conmigo!, Chapter 6

Scripts *for* Quizzes 6-1B, 6-2B, 6-3B

Quiz 6-1B Capítulo 6 Primer paso

I. Listening

  A.   1. Juana es mi tía.
        2. Pilar es la hermana de José.
        3. Rosa es mi abuela.
        4. Julia y Elena son mis primas.
        5. Juana es la abuela de Pedro.

Quiz 6-2B Capítulo 6 Segundo paso

I. Listening

  A.   1. A veces son muy traviesos. Uno de ellos es delgado y el otro es gordo.
        2. Tiene ochenta años pero se ve joven. Tiene los ojos azules y el pelo blanco.
        3. Son personas muy especiales. Uno es alto y pelirrojo. Una es baja y un poco gorda.
        4. Es delgado y tiene los ojos de color café con pelo negro.
        5. Esta chica es pelirroja con ojos azules y es bastante delgada.

Quiz 6-3B Capítulo 6 Tercer paso

I. Listening

  A. En mi casa hay mucho que hacer y todos ayudamos a mamá. Primero hago la cama y después paso la aspiradora. Mi mamá prepara el desayuno para nosotros y comemos juntos. Después del desayuno, mi papá limpia la cocina y luego mi hermano Pedro saca la basura. Por la tarde, mi hermana Juana trabaja con mamá en el jardín. Después de todo eso, la casa está en orden y todos descansamos un rato.

CAPÍTULO 6

Answers to Quizzes 6-1A, 6-1B

ANSWERS Quiz 6-1A

A. (10 points: 1 point per item)
1. abuela
2. hermana
3. primos
4. tía
5. padre
6. hijo
7. esposa
8. abuelo
9. prima
10. madre

B. (9 points: 1.5 points per item)
11. Geraldo
12. Elisa
13. Geraldo
14. Pedro
15. Pascual
16. Clara

C. (16 points: 2 points per item)
17. nuestra madre
18. Mis padres
19. Nuestros perros
20. mi madrastra
21. Sus hijos
22. mis hermanastros
23. Su padre
24. Sus primos

ANSWERS Quiz 6-1B

I. Listening

A. (10 points: 2 points per item)
1. sí
2. no
3. no
4. sí
5. no

II. Reading

B. (8 points: 2 points per item)
6. sí
7. no
8. sí
9. sí

III. Writing

C. (12 points: 4 points per item)
Answers will vary. Possible answers:
10. Pilar es morena y baja. A ella le gusta escuchar música.
11. Jaime toca bien el piano. Es muy artístico.
12. Santiago es guapo y cómico. A él le gusta leer el periódico.

IV. Culture

D. (5 points: 2.5 points per item)
13. a
14. a

ANSWERS Quiz 6-2A

A. (12 points: 1 point per item)
1. cómo son
2. listos
3. mayor
4. menor
5. travieso
6. De qué color es
7. pelirrojo
8. ojos
9. viejos
10. canas
11. se ve
12. atractiva

B. (8 points: 1 point per item)
13. pelirrojos
14. gorda
15. traviesas
16. altos, delgados
17. atractivas
18. jóvenes
19. listos

C. (9 points: 1.5 points per item)
20. hacemos
21. hago
22. hace
23. salimos
24. salgo
25. salen

D. (6 points: 1 point per item)
26. x   29. x
27. a   30. a
28. x   31. a

ANSWERS Quiz 6-2B

I. Listening

A. (10 points: 2 points per item)
1. c
2. a
3. b
4. d
5. e

II. Reading

B. (10 points: 2 points per item)
6. c
7. a
8. b
9. c
10. b

III. Writing

C. (12 points: 3 points per item)
11. Salgo de Nueva York el quince de junio.
12. Soy bajo/a, moreno/a y delgado/a.
13. Quiero visitar a mi amigo Rodolfo cuando estoy en Guatemala.
14. Quiero visitar unas ruinas también.

IV. Culture

D. (3 points: 1 point per item)
15. a
16. a
17. b

C A P Í T U L O 6

ANSWERS Quiz 6-3A

A. (8 points: 1 point per item)
1. Debo
2. Debes
3. debemos
4. deben
5. debe
6. deben
7. debo
8. debemos

B. (16 points: 1 point per item)
9. debe, cortar
10. debemos, hacer
11. debo, limpiar
12. debe, pasar
13. deben, poner
14. debe, cuidar
15. Debo, planchar
16. debemos, trabajar

C. (6 points: 1 point per item)
17. pone
18. pongo
19. ponen
20. pone
21. ponemos
22. poner

ANSWERS Quiz 6-3B

I. Listening

A. (10 points: 2 points per item)
1. d
2. b
3. c
4. e
5. a

II. Reading

B. (8 points: 2 points per item)
6. sí
7. no
8. sí
9. no

III. Writing

C. (12 points: 2 points per items)
10. Tú debes cuidar al gato.
11. Ella debe limpiar la sala.
12. Nosotros debemos poner la mesa.
13. Ellos deben limpiar la cocina.
14. Yo debo cortar el césped.
15. Ustedes deben planchar la ropa.

CAPÍTULO 6

Scripts for Chapter 6 Test

I. Listening

A. Hola, me llamo Ana. Vivo en la ciudad de Concepción, Chile. Quiero presentarles a mi familia. Primero, a mi mamá. Se llama Olga. Es muy cariñosa y amable. Mi padre se llama Eduardo. Es cariñoso también pero un poco estricto. Mi tía Elsa y mi tío Luis viven en Valparaíso. Son muy simpáticos. Me gusta mucho visitarlos. Tienen una hija, mi prima Teresa. Mis abuelos viven en Valparaíso también. Mi abuela se llama Luisa Gómez de Pérez. Son muy cariñosos. Son viejos pero se ven muy jóvenes. Mi hermano mayor es Jorge. Es muy inteligente. Asiste a la universidad. Mi hermano menor se llama Eduardo. Lo quiero mucho, pero es un poco travieso. Bueno, ésta es mi familia. Somos todos muy unidos.

B. 6. — ¿Qué debes hacer en casa hoy?
       — Debo cuidar al gato.
    7. — ¿Qué hago para ayudar, papá?
       — ¿Por qué no cortas el césped?
    8. — ¿Pones la mesa hoy, Juan?
       — Sí, papá. Pongo la mesa todos los lunes.
    9. — A mi hermana María le gusta pasar la aspiradora.
       — Sí, me gusta porque soy muy organizada.

Answers to Chapter 6 Test

I. Listening Maximum Score: 30 points

A. (15 points: 3 points per item)   **B.** (15 points: 3 points per item)

1. e	6. c
2. d	7. a
3. a	8. b
4. c	9. d
5. b	10. b

II. Reading Maximum Score: 30 points

C. (15 points: 3 points per item)   **D.** (15 points: 3 points per item)

11. c	16. b
12. a	17. d
13. c	18. a
14. c	19. d
15. b	20. c

III. Culture Maximum Score: 12 points

E. (6 points: 3 points per item)   **F.** (6 points: 3 points per item)

21. a   23. and 24. Answers will vary but should include: life-long
22. b   relationship, provide affection, advice, occasional
                                    support with school or careers. Having godpar-
                                    ents increases the extended family.

IV. Writing Maximum Score: 28 points

G. (15 points: 3 points per item)
Answers will vary. Possible answers:

25. Éste es mi padre. Es muy alto y muy cómico.
26. Ésta es mi mamá. Es muy cariñosa y muy bonita.
27. Éste es mi hermano menor. Es muy divertido y un poco travieso.
28. Ésta es mi hermana menor. Es muy joven y muy bonita.
29. Éste es mi hermano mayor. Es muy inteligente y delgado.

H. (13 points)
Answers will vary. Possible answer:

30. Hay muchas cosas que hacer y necesito tu ayuda. Debes cuidar al gato, limpiar la mesa y lavar la ropa. También debes planchar la ropa, pasar la aspiradora y hacer la cama. Gracias, hermano.

CAPÍTULO 6

I. Listening

Maximum Score: 20 points

A. Listen as Gloria and Juan discuss their school subjects. Then answer the following questions based on their conversation. (5 points)

_____ 1. ¿Cómo está Gloria?
    a. bastante mal
    b. estupenda
    c. bien

_____ 2. ¿Qué clase le gusta a Juan?
    a. el inglés
    b. el francés
    c. la biología

_____ 3. ¿Por qué no le gusta a Gloria la clase de francés?
    a. Es mala.
    b. Es aburrida.
    c. Es difícil.

_____ 4. ¿A qué hora es la clase de francés?
    a. A la una.
    b. Son las ocho.
    c. A las ocho.

_____ 5. Juan tiene prisa porque su clase de baile está _____.
    a. bastante lejos
    b. atrasada
    c. muy cerca

SCORE _____

B. Listen to the following statements and decide if they are **a) logical** or **b) illogical**. (5 points)

_____ 6.

_____ 7.

_____ 8.

_____ 9.

_____ 10.

SCORE _____

C. What is everybody talking about? Match each topic with the correct conversation. (5 points)

_____ 11.

_____ 12.

_____ 13.

_____ 14.

_____ 15.

a. free-time activities
b. family members
c. household chores
d. school subjects
e. weather

SCORE [   ]

D. Listen as Mercedes describes her friends. Then match each name with the correct picture. (5 points)

a.   b.   c.   d.   e.

_____ 16. Luisa

_____ 17. Mario

_____ 18. Beto

_____ 19. Dolores

_____ 20. Jaime

SCORE [   ]

II. Reading

Maximum Score: 25 points

A. Read the following questions and choose the best answer for each one. (5 points)

_____ 21. ¿Cuántos años tienes?

_____ 22. ¿Qué les gusta hacer después de clases?

_____ 23. ¿De dónde es Maribel?

_____ 24. ¿Qué tiempo hace?

_____ 25. ¿Cómo te llamas?

a. Es de Sevilla.
b. Margarita, ¿y tú?
c. Está lloviendo.
d. Tengo quince años.
e. Nos gusta ir al centro comercial.

SCORE [   ]

Spanish 1 ¡Ven conmigo!, Midterm Exam

B. Juan and Ana meet in the hallway after school. Put their conversation in the correct order. (5 points)

_____ 26.

_____ 27.

_____ 28.

_____ 29.

_____ 30.

a. ¿Historia? Yo también. ¿Por qué no estudiamos juntos? Es más divertido, ¿no?
b. Hola, Juan. ¿Qué tal?
c. ¡Buena idea! ¡Vamos!
d. Yo necesito estudiar también porque tengo un examen de historia mañana.
e. Regular. Tengo dos exámenes mañana. Necesito estudiar pero no quiero.

SCORE _____

C. Read about Amalia's family. Then decide if the statements that follow are a) **true** or b) **false**. (5 points)

Amalia tiene una familia bastante grande y unida. Tiene una hermana menor, sus abuelos y muchos tíos y primos. Todos viven en la misma ciudad. Sus abuelos viven al lado de la familia. El tío Jaime y la tía Adriana viven muy cerca también en una casa grande con una piscina. Tienen tres hijos — Marcos, Patricia y Cristina. La tía Luisa no tiene hijos, pero tiene dos perros y un gato. Es profesora de inglés. Toda la familia visita a los abuelos los domingos por la tarde. Además, cada invierno la familia de Amalia, los abuelos, los tíos y los primos hacen un viaje a las montañas de Colorado. A todos les gusta esquiar aunque el papá de Amalia no sabe esquiar muy bien. Amalia tiene una hermana menor que se llama Josefina. A Josefina le gusta asistir a la escuela y practicar deportes.

_____ 31. Amalia's family likes to do things together.

_____ 32. One of Amalia's uncles teaches English.

_____ 33. Amalia rarely sees her grandparents.

_____ 34. Josefina is younger than Amalia.

_____ 35. No one in Amalia's family likes cold weather.

SCORE _____

Nombre _____ Clase _____ Fecha _____

D. Look at this TV guide and decide if the statements below are **a) true** or **b) false**. The times are based on a twenty-four-hour clock, so that 13:00 is 1:00 p.m., for example. (5 points)

6:00 6:30	Buenos días agricultor	Despertares Esta mañana	Noticiero Telem.	NBC News	Dibujos Club 700	Buenos días Euronews
7:00 7:30	Primera hora Protagonistas	Deporte total	La noticia Copa	Contacto directo	Noti 10	Aprendiendo a vivir Noticiero
8:00 8:30	Mucho gusto	Vanidades Teve	Club telemundo	Tiro libre Complicidades	Acción de Noti 10 D'Cocina	Telediario Telenegocios
9:00 9:30	Para usted Dibujos	Toque de Mariaca Cine: A veces se	Animados	Gino Mollinari	El mundo infantil de TC	Directo Tve TV mandato
10:00 10:30	Clásicos del cine mexicano	dice una mentira		Princesa		Euronews TV mandato
11:00 11:30		La traidora	Cara a cara: Me visto como me	Por estas calles	TC cine: Idilio presente	Mundo de cada día Primera respuesta
12:00 12:30	Gasparín Protagonistas	Deporte total	da la gana Primer impacto	Telebreves Bonanza		Lingo
13:00 13:30	Polivoces Medio día	24 horas	El Pirrurris Aló que tal	Televistazo Video Show	Noti 10 Sintonizando	Telenegocios Deutsche Welle
14:00 14:30	En familia con Mercedes	Aquí Mariela Marielena		Cuando llega el	Geraldo: Los	Tventas Aventura del saber
15:00 15:30	Alcanzar una estrella	Inés Duarte	Ocurrió así	amor Señora	dobles de los famosos	
16:00 16:30	Deportes espectaculares	Club de Disney	Cristina	Liveman	El engaño	Sinvergüenza Deutsche welle
17:00 17:30		Supercampeones Carrusel	Feria de la alegría	Yo amo a Lucy Chapulín	Potra Zaina	TV mandato

"Teleagenda" from *Hoy*, Tuesday, May 3, 1994. Copyright © 1994 by Editores e Impresores S.A. Reprinted by permission of **Editores e Impresores S.A.**

_____ **36.** Si te gustan el tenis y el fútbol, hay un programa interesante a las siete y media de la mañana.

_____ **37.** Si quieres ver una película, debes mirar la tele a las diez de la mañana.

_____ **38.** No hay programas de deportes por la tarde.

_____ **39.** Si te gusta preparar la cena, hay un programa para ti a las ocho y media.

_____ **40.** Te gustan los videos; a la una y media hay un programa para ti.

SCORE _____

E. Read the descriptions of Guillermo's classmates on page 161. Then match each drawing with the passage that correctly describes each person. (5 points)

a.

b.

c.

d.

e.

Spanish 1 ¡Ven conmigo!, Midterm Exam

MIDTERM EXAM

_____ 41. Mi amigo David es muy alto y delgado. Le gustan muchos deportes, por ejemplo, el fútbol, el tenis y la natación. Todos los fines de semana va al parque a jugar al tenis.

_____ 42. A Pat le encanta la música clásica. Es inteligente y muy trabajadora. Toca la guitarra muy bien porque practica todos los días.

_____ 43. Eugenio es bajo y muy atlético. Practica deportes después de clases con sus amigos. Ahora está en el parque.

_____ 44. Chris es buen cocinero y ayuda a preparar la comida en casa. Me gusta comer todo lo que prepara.

_____ 45. Marcos es guapo y romántico. Tiene muchos amigos y a ellos les gusta cantar mientras Marcos toca sus canciones favoritas.

SCORE [   ]

III. Culture

Maximum Score: 10 points

A. Read the statements below. Based on the information in your textbook, determine whether the statements are a) **true** or b) **false**. (5 points)

_____ 46. It's possible to go snow-skiing in parts of South America in July.

_____ 47. It's very common for teens in Spanish-speaking countries to get cars on their sixteenth birthdays.

_____ 48. If you looked for Francisco Javier López Aguilar in a phone book, you would look under **L**.

_____ 49. Students in Spanish-speaking countries take 5–6 classes daily, like students in the United States.

_____ 50. Most teenagers in Spanish-speaking countries have phones and TV sets in their bedrooms.

SCORE [   ]

B. Write five cultural facts you have learned about Spanish-speaking countries or people. You may choose from the following categories: sports, transportation, grading scales, greetings among friends, or interpersonal space. (5 points)

51. _____

52. _____

53. _____

54. _____

55. _____

SCORE [   ]

Nombre _____ Clase _____ Fecha _____

IV. Writing
Maximum Score: 45 points

A. For each item below, write a complete sentence in Spanish telling how you would ask for or give the information indicated. (10 points)

How would you . . . ?

56. ask a friend what the new math teacher is like

_____

57. ask a classmate if he or she likes sports

_____

58. tell your mom or dad you don't want to eat because you're not hungry

_____

59. ask what time it is

_____

60. ask a new friend how many people there are in his or her family

_____

SCORE [   ]

B. Answer the following questions in complete sentences. (10 points)

61. ¿Cuántos años tienes?

_____

62. ¿Qué te gusta hacer los fines de semana?

_____

63. ¿Qué tiempo hace hoy?

_____

64. ¿De qué color son tus ojos?

_____

65. ¿De dónde eres?

_____

SCORE [   ]

Spanish 1 ¡Ven conmigo!, Midterm Exam

C. Look at the drawing and then answer the questions below in complete Spanish sentences. (10 points)

66. Name at least three things that are in the bedroom.

_____

67. What is the girl in the living room doing?

_____

68. The woman in the kitchen is preparing a meal, but what two chores should she do next?

_____

69. What two things does the girl who is studying need to do? Her room's a mess!

_____

70. What's the weather like today?

_____

SCORE [   ]

D. Write a paragraph of at least five sentences about your school. Include the following elements: where your school is in relation to your house, what time your first class starts, what your favorite class is, what your best friends are like, and what you and your friends like to do after school. (15 points)

71. _____

_____

_____

_____

_____

_____

_____

_____

_____

SCORE [   ]

TOTAL SCORE [   ] /100

Nombre _____ Clase _____ Fecha _____

Circle the letter that matches the most appropriate response.

I. Listening
Maximum Score: 20 points

A. (5 points)

1. a b c
2. a b c
3. a b c
4. a b c
5. a b c

SCORE [＿＿＿]

B. (5 points)

6. a b
7. a b
8. a b
9. a b
10. a b

SCORE [＿＿＿]

C. (5 points)

11. a b c d e
12. a b c d e
13. a b c d e
14. a b c d e
15. a b c d e

SCORE [＿＿＿]

D. (5 points)

16. a b c d e
17. a b c d e
18. a b c d e
19. a b c d e
20. a b c d e

SCORE [＿＿＿]

II. Reading
Maximum Score: 25 points

A. (5 points)

21. a b c d e
22. a b c d e
23. a b c d e
24. a b c d e
25. a b c d e

SCORE [＿＿＿]

B. (5 points)

26. a b c d e
27. a b c d e
28. a b c d e
29. a b c d e
30. a b c d e

SCORE [＿＿＿]

C. (5 points)

31. a b
32. a b
33. a b
34. a b
35. a b

SCORE [＿＿＿]

D. (5 points)

36. a b
37. a b
38. a b
39. a b
40. a b

SCORE [＿＿＿]

E. (5 points)

41. a b c d e
42. a b c d e
43. a b c d e
44. a b c d e
45. a b c d e

SCORE [＿＿＿]

MIDTERM EXAM

III. Culture

Maximum Score: 10 points

A. (5 points)

46. a b

47. a b

48. a b

49. a b

50. a b

SCORE [   ]

B. (5 points)

51. _____

52. _____

53. _____

54. _____

55. _____

SCORE [   ]

IV. Writing

Maximum Score: 45 points

A. (10 points)

56. _____

57. _____

58. _____

59. _____

60. _____

SCORE [   ]

Spanish 1 ¡Ven conmigo!, Midterm Exam

B. (10 points)

61. _____

62. _____

63. _____

64. _____

65. _____

SCORE [   ]

C. (10 points)

66. _____

67. _____

68. _____

69. _____

70. _____

SCORE [   ]

D. (15 points)

71. _____

_____

_____

_____

_____

_____

_____

_____

_____

_____

_____

_____

_____

SCORE [   ]

TOTAL SCORE [   ] /100

Listening Scripts for Midterm Exam

MIDTERM EXAM

I. Listening

A.

GLORIA	¡Hola, Juan! ¿Qué tal?
JUAN	Bien, ¿y tú, Gloria?
GLORIA	Estoy bien. ¿Te gustan las clases nuevas?
JUAN	Sí. Mi clase favorita es la clase de inglés porque me gustan los idiomas. Y a ti, ¿te gustan tus clases?
GLORIA	Sí, más o menos, pero no me gusta la clase de francés porque es muy aburrida. Además, es demasiado temprano. Es a las ocho de la mañana.
JUAN	Oye, Gloria. No tengo reloj. ¿Qué hora es?
GLORIA	A ver... ya son las cuatro.
JUAN	Ay, estoy atrasado. Mi clase de baile es a las cuatro y media. Está muy lejos de aquí y necesito tomar el autobús.
GLORIA	¡Date prisa! Nos vemos mañana.

B.
6. Debes estudiar esta noche porque tienes un examen mañana.
7. Cuando necesito comprar cuadernos y libros voy a la librería.
8. Es divertido nadar cuando hace mucho calor.
9. Mi hermana tiene cinco años. Yo tengo quince años. Ella es mi hermana mayor.
10. Me gusta practicar deportes cuando estoy en la biblioteca.

168 Testing Program

Spanish 1 ¡Ven conmigo!, Midterm Exam

Copyright © by Holt, Rinehart and Winston. All rights reserved.

Listening Scripts for Midterm Exam

C. 11.   ANA   Juanita, ¿qué clases tienes este semestre?
      JUANITA   Tengo química, geometría, educación física, inglés, español y computación. ¿Y tú?
      ANA   Tengo álgebra, geografía, inglés, arte, ciencias sociales y francés.

  12.   FELIPE   Jorge, ¿ayudas mucho en casa?
      JORGE   Claro, hombre. Pongo la mesa, saco la basura y corto el césped.
      FELIPE   ¡Qué trabajador! Oye, ¿quieres limpiar mi cuarto?

  13.   DINORA   ¿Qué hacen ustedes después de clases?
      SILVIA   Depende, pero muchas veces vamos a tomar algo en un café o montamos en bicicleta.

  14.   MELVIN   Es un buen día para ir al parque a jugar al fútbol, ¿verdad?
      ENRIQUE   No, Melvin. Hace frío y va a llover.

  15.   SANDRA   ¿Cuántos hermanos tienes?
      ERNESTO   Un hermano. No tengo una familia grande. Somos cuatro—mi mamá, mi papá y mi hermano mayor.

D. MERCEDES   ¿Cómo son mis amigos? A ver... Mi amiga Luisa es bonita, morena y muy activa. Le encanta bailar. Mario es alto y delgado. Le encanta jugar al baloncesto. Beto es guapo y moreno. Es un amigo muy divertido. Dolores tiene el pelo largo y es delgada. Le gusta descansar y hablar con amigos. Y Jaime, pues Jaime es mi mejor amigo. Es guapo y moreno. Todos los fines de semana montamos en bicicleta juntos.

Answers to **Midterm Exam**

I. Listening Maximum Score: 20 points

A. (5 points: 1 point per item)
1. c
2. a
3. b
4. c
5. a

B. (5 points: 1 point per item)
6. a
7. a
8. a
9. b
10. b

C. (5 points: 1 point per item)
11. d
12. c
13. a
14. e
15. b

D. (5 points: 1 point per item)
16. d
17. b
18. a
19. e
20. c

II. Reading Maximum Score: 25 points

A. (5 points: 1 point per item)
21. d
22. e
23. a
24. c
25. b

B. (5 points: 1 point per item)
26. b
27. e
28. d
29. a
30. c

C. (5 points: 1 point per item)
31. a
32. b
33. b
34. a
35. b

D. (5 points: 1 point per item)
36. a
37. a
38. b
39. a
40. a

E. (5 points: 1 point per item)
41. c
42. b
43. a
44. e
45. d

III. Culture Maximum Score: 10 points

A. (5 points: 1 point per item)
46. a
47. b
48. a
49. b
50. b

B. (5 points: 1 point per item)
Answers will vary for items 51 to 55. Possible answers:
51. Soccer and tennis are popular sports in Spanish-speaking countries.
52. Fewer young people own cars in Spain or Latin America than in the United States.
53. Mexican schools use a grading scale of 1 to 10; 6 is passing.
54. Spanish speakers often greet each other with a handshake or a kiss.
55. In Spain, most people live in apartments; bedrooms are smaller and sisters or brothers will sometimes have to share a room.

IV. Writing Maximum Score: 45 points

A. (10 points: 2 points per item)
56. ¿Cómo es el/la nuevo(a) profesor(a) de matemáticas?
57. ¿Te gustan los deportes?
58. Mamá, no quiero comer porque no tengo hambre.
59. ¿Qué hora es, por favor?
60. ¿Cuántas personas hay en tu familia?

B. (10 points: 2 points per item)
Answers will vary for items 61 to 65.

C. (10 points: 2 points per item)
Answers will vary for items 66 to 70.

D. (15 points: 3 points per sentence) Answers will vary for item 71. Possible answers:
La escuela está cerca de mi casa. Mi primera clase comienza a las ocho y veinte.
Mi clase favorita es la biología. Mis amigos son simpáticos y divertidos. Después
de clases nos gusta ir a un café a tomar algo.

Spanish 1 ¡Ven conmigo!, Midterm Exam

Nombre _____ Clase _____ Fecha _____

¿Qué te gustaría hacer?

PRIMER PASO

Maximum Score: 30

Grammar and Vocabulary

A. Complete the descriptions of people's activities with the correct forms of the verb in parentheses. (8 points)

— Típicamente yo **1.** _____ (empezar) la tarea a las cuatro y media. A veces mi amiga

Beatriz **2.** _____ (venir) a casa a estudiar conmigo. Nosotros **3.** _____

(preferir) escuchar la radio cuando estudiamos.

— La fiesta de Victoria **4.** _____ (empezar) a las ocho. Sus primas Rosario y Leonor

5. _____ (venir) a la fiesta, pero ellas **6.** _____ (preferir) llegar un poco

tarde, a las nueve.

— Gregorio, el sábado tú **7.** _____ (empezar) con tu nueva clase de arte, ¿verdad?

¿Qué **8.** _____ (preferir) hacer en tu tiempo libre, dibujar o pintar?

SCORE [   ]

B. Natalia and Esteban are making plans for this afternoon. Complete their conversation with the correct forms of the verbs **empezar**, **preferir**, and **venir**. (12 points)

NATALIA   Esteban, voy al cine esta tarde. ¿Quieres ir conmigo?

ESTEBAN   ¿A qué hora **9.** _____ la película?

NATALIA   A las cinco.

ESTEBAN   Pues... gracias, pero yo **10.** _____ ir contigo otro día, si es posible. Hoy

después de clase Marcos y Tania **11.** _____ a mi casa a estudiar para el

examen de historia.

NATALIA   Pero el examen de historia es el jueves, y hoy es lunes. ¿Por qué

12. _____ ustedes a estudiar hoy? Todavía es muy temprano, ¿no?

ESTEBAN   Pues, los exámenes de historia siempre son difíciles, y nosotros **13.** _____

estar preparados. Oye, ¿por qué no **14.** _____ tú a mi casa también?

NATALIA   Bueno, de acuerdo. ¿Está bien si yo **15.** _____ a las cuatro?

ESTEBAN   Perfecto, entonces nosotros **16.** _____ a estudiar a las cuatro y quince.

SCORE [   ]

Spanish 1 ¡Ven conmigo!, Chapter 7

Testing Program **171**

Quiz 7-1A

C. Different members of Martín's family are returning home from excursions. Write out his explanations of where each person or group is coming from, using the correct forms of **venir** and the Spanish words for the places pictured. (10 points)

17. Luisa y yo

_____

_____

18. Mamá y Papá

_____

_____

19. Tomasito

_____

_____

20. Belén

_____

_____

21. mis primos

_____

_____

SCORE ☐

TOTAL SCORE ☐ /30

¿Qué te gustaría hacer?

Quiz 7-1 B

PRIMER PASO

Maximum Score: 30

I. Listening

A. Listen to Juan ask questions or make statements and choose the response that makes the most sense. (10 points)

_____ 1. **a.** Sí, pero quiero ir a la piscina también.
       b. Sí, me gustaría ir al partido de fútbol.

_____ 2. **a.** Sí, vamos a la biblioteca a la una.
       b. Sí, quiero estudiar con Alicia.

_____ 3. **a.** Sí, está en la tienda.
       b. Lo siento, pero está en el centro comercial.

_____ 4. **a.** No, no me gusta ir al museo.
       b. Sí, me gustan los animales.

_____ 5. **a.** Claro que sí.
       b. Bueno, llamo más tarde.

SCORE [____]

II. Reading

B. Read this telephone conversation between Alfredo and Silvia. Then answer the questions that follow in English. (10 points)

SILVIA   Buenas tardes.
ALFREDO   Hola, Silvia. Habla Alfredo. ¿Quieres venir a mi casa a mirar la televisión y estudiar después?
SILVIA   No, gracias. Pilar y yo vamos al parque de atracciones. ¿Quieres ir con nosotras?
ALFREDO   Gracias, pero es imposible. Hay un examen de matemáticas mañana y necesito estudiar.
SILVIA   Pues, yo no tengo exámenes mañana y no necesito estudiar. El sábado voy al teatro. ¿Quieres ir conmigo?
ALFREDO   Sí, ¿a qué hora empieza la obra *(play)*?
SILVIA   A las dos. ¿Está bien?
ALFREDO   Sí, hasta el sábado. Adiós, Silvia.

6. What does Alfredo invite Silvia to do?

_____

7. Does she accept his invitation?

_____

Quiz 7-1B

8. What are Silvia's plans?

____

9. Why doesn't Alfredo go with Silvia and Pilar?

____

10. What plans are made for Saturday?

____

SCORE

III. Writing

C. Read the following telephone conversation between Berta and Francisco and fill in the missing information. (10 points)

11. BERTA ____.

FRANCISCO Hola, Berta. ¿Cómo estás?

BERTA ¿Quién habla?

12. FRANCISCO ____.

13. ¿____?

BERTA Lo siento, pero Luisa no está.

14. ¿____?

FRANCISCO Sí, pregúntale *(ask her)* si le gustaría ir al parque de atracciones este fin de semana. ¿A ti te gustaría ir también? Te invito.

15. BERTA ____.

FRANCISCO ¡Qué bueno! Pues, no olvides *(don't forget)* darle el recado a Silvia. Hasta luego, Berta.

BERTA Adiós.

SCORE

TOTAL SCORE /30

¿Qué te gustaría hacer?

SEGUNDO PASO

Maximum Score: 35

Grammar and Vocabulary

A. Your friend Mónica sent you a note about what everyone is doing for the surprise party for a classmate. Complete the note with the correct form of **pensar**. (9 points)

¡Hola! Tú, ¿qué **1.** _____ hacer para la fiesta? Maricela y yo **2.** _____

comprar la comida. Yo también **3.** _____ invitar a unos amigos. Vicente y Tania

4. _____ limpiar la sala. Y Norma **5.** _____ tocar la guitarra. La fiesta es a las

ocho en punto, pero todos nosotros **6.** _____ estar allí a las ocho menos cuarto.

SCORE [   ]

B. Alida and Raquel are talking about weekend plans. Complete their conversation about what is going to happen, using the correct form of the expression **ir + a** and a logical infinitive. Some infinitives may be used more than once. (7 points)

asistir	tener	hacer	ir	visitar
		ver		

ALIDA   ¿Qué haces este fin de semana? ¿**7.** _____ a tus abuelos?

RAQUEL   Sí. Mis primos y yo **8.** _____ una fiesta grande para mi abuela. Ella

9. _____ 80 años. ¿Y qué planes tienes tú?

ALIDA   **10.** _____ al parque de atracciones con Cristina el sábado. Después,

creo que nosotras **11.** _____ una película.

RAQUEL   ¿Y alguien más **12.** _____ con ustedes?

ALIDA   No. Leticia necesita ir a una boda. Y creo que Pablo y Nuria

13. _____ a un concierto.

SCORE [   ]

Nombre _____ Clase _____ Fecha _____

 Quiz 7-2A

C. Raimundo is talking to his family while everyone gets ready to go out. Complete what he says with the correct missing verb. Use each verb only once. (10 points)

| peinarte | lavarte los dientes | afeitarme |
| ducharse | | maquillarse |

Marta, date prisa porque yo todavía necesito 14. _____. Mamá todavía

quiere 15. _____, y creo que Papá necesita 16. _____ después.

Susi, ¿qué comes? Necesitas 17. _____ ahora mismo. ¡Y mira tu pelo! Vas a

18. _____ ahora, ¿verdad?

SCORE [ ]

D. Sergio is talking about everyone's daily routine. Complete each sentence with the correct form of the underlined verb. Remember to use the correct reflexive pronoun. (9 points)

19. Mi hermano prefiere <u>lavarse</u> los dientes antes de desayunar. Yo prefiero

_____ los dientes después.

20. Prefiero <u>ducharme</u> por la mañana. Elzbieta, ¿cuándo quieres _____? ¿Y

cuándo necesita _____ Lupe?

21. Los fines de semana, mi hermano prefiere no <u>afeitarse</u>. Pero mi papá necesita

_____ todos los días.

22. Mi hermana prefiere <u>maquillarse</u> todos los días. Pero mi mamá prefiere

_____ sólo para las fiestas. Y tú, Carla, a ti no te gusta

_____, ¿verdad?

SCORE [ ]

TOTAL SCORE [/35]

CAPÍTULO 7

Spanish 1 ¡Ven conmigo!, Chapter 7

7 ¿Qué te gustaría hacer?

SEGUNDO PASO

Maximum Score: 35

I. Listening

A. Look at the following pictures. Listen as Arturo tells you something about each of them. Then write the letter of the picture that he describes. (10 points)

a.   b.   c.   d.   e.

1. _____   2. _____   3. _____   4. _____   5. _____

SCORE _____

II. Reading

B. Read the comic strip. Then indicate who would make each of the following statements by writing **Calvin** or **mamá** in each blank. (10 points)

engrudo *paste*   **te acordaras** *you would remember*   **Te lo pusiste** *You put it*   **¡Ven para acá!** *Come here!*
                         Apúrate=Date prisa   **así** *this way*

_____ **6.** Necesitas lavarte el pelo y luego peinarte.

_____ **7.** Me gusta peinarme el pelo con engrudo.

_____ **8.** Voy a tener el pelo más bonito del colegio.

Quiz 7-2B

_____ 9. Pienso peinarme el pelo así todo el tiempo.

_____ 10. Vamos a lavarte el pelo ahora.

SCORE [ ]

III. Writing

C. Read the following question. Then write sentences in Spanish to complete the questionnaire on grooming. (10 points)

> When does each person usually need to do the following activities:
> In the morning, afternoon, or evening?

11. comb your hair (you)

_____

12. take a shower (you)

_____

13. shave (your father)

_____

14. put on makeup (your mother)

_____

15. brush his or her teeth (your friend)

_____

SCORE [ ]

IV. Culture

D. Based on the information in your textbook, answer **a) cierto** or **b) falso** to the statements below. (5 points)

_____ 16. In Spain and Latin America, public transportation is used more frequently than private cars.

_____ 17. The cost of a car is about the same all over the world.

SCORE [ ]

TOTAL SCORE [ ] /35

¿Qué te gustaría hacer?

■ TERCER PASO

Grammar and Vocabulary

A. Ricardo and Daniel are trying to make plans for the weekend. Complete their conversation with the missing expressions. Each expression will be used only once. (7 points)

| Qué lástima | ocupado | cita | lo siento |
| | tengo planes | | Tal vez | Te gustaría |

RICARDO   Daniel, ¿qué haces el sábado? ¿1. _____ ir conmigo al partido?

DANIEL   Gracias, pero ya 2. _____ para el sábado.

¿3. _____ el domingo?

RICARDO   Ay, 4. _____ , pero el domingo es imposible. Estoy

5. _____ todo el día. Y por la noche tengo una

6. _____ con Marisa.

DANIEL   ¡7. _____! Pues, otro día entonces.

SCORE [   ]

B. Read each sentence. Then, use an expression with **tener** to complete the summarizing statements in Spanish. Remember to use the correct form of **tener**. (18 points)

8. Eva and Paloma have class at 2:15. It's now 2:14.

   Ellas _____.

9. You and your friends would love to go for pizza after class.

   Nosotros _____ comer pizza.

10. Your friend has a big math test tomorrow.

   Él _____ estudiar mucho esta noche.

11. Rogelio and Felipe have to practice for the meet on Saturday.

   Ellos _____ practicar.

CAPÍTULO 7

Quiz 7-3A

12. Last night you stayed up until 3:00.

    Hoy _____ mucho _____.

13. Eduardo has a cavity every time he goes to the dentist.

    Él _____ lavarse los dientes más.

14. Your friend Martha has her 16th birthday today.

    Hoy ella _____ 16 _____.

15. Sofía and Guille would love to go to the mall after school.

    Ellos _____ comprar ropa nueva.

16. You woke up late, and need to shower and get dressed in ten minutes.

    Yo _____ mucha _____.

SCORE [ ]

C. This weekend, everyone has responsibilities that conflict with their fun plans. First explain what everyone feels like doing, then write what that person or group has to do. Use the correct expressions with **tener** and the infinitives in parentheses. (10 points)

17. el profesor (ir al campo, trabajar)

    _____, pero _____.

18. yo (ver una película, cuidar a mi hermanita)

    _____, pero _____.

19. mis amigos y yo (comer hamburguesas, estudiar)

    _____, pero _____.

20. tú (tomar un refresco, organizar tu cuarto)

    _____, pero _____.

21. Víctor y Ana (asistir al baile, visitar a sus tíos)

    _____, pero _____.

SCORE [ ]

TOTAL SCORE [ ] /35

Spanish 1 ¡Ven conmigo!, Chapter 7

Nombre _____ Clase _____ Fecha _____

7 ¿Qué te gustaría hacer?

Quiz 7-3B

■ TERCER PASO

Maximum Score: 35

I. Listening

A. First read the responses below. Then you'll hear five invitations. Choose the best response for each invitation. (10 points)

    a. Sí, cómo no. ¿A qué hora empieza el partido?
    b. ¡Qué lástima! Me gusta la música, pero tengo que trabajar.
    c. Necesito estudiar más, pero no quiero. Tengo mucho sueño.
    d. Lo siento, pero ya tengo planes para el sábado.
    e. Me gustaría cenar contigo, pero estoy muy ocupado en casa ahora.

1. _____   2. _____   3. _____   4. _____   5. _____   SCORE [   ]

II. Reading

B. Mónica just received an invitation from Severiano for this weekend. Read her note and then answer the questions that follow in English. (10 points)

> Querido Severiano,
> Muchas gracias por invitarme al baile este sábado por la noche. ¡Cuánto me gustaría ir! Lo siento, pero este sábado no puedo. Tengo muchas cosas que hacer por la tarde. Mi mamá está enferma, así que tengo que cuidar a mi hermanito. También necesito estudiar para un examen y ayudar en casa. Debo pasar la aspiradora y organizar mi cuarto. Después de hacer todo eso, voy a estar cansada y no voy a tener ganas de salir. Gracias por la invitación. Tal vez otro día, ¿no?
>
>   Tu amiga,
>   Mónica

6. Where does Severiano invite Monica to go and on what day?

_____

_____

Quiz 7-3B

7. What's the main reason Monica gives for not being able to go?

_____

_____

8. Name two things that Monica has to do on Saturday.

_____

_____

9. Is Monica going to be busy during the dance itself? Explain.

_____

_____

10. What does Monica suggest at the end of her letter?

_____

_____

SCORE [   ]

III. Writing

C. You have received a lot of invitations this week! Reply to each, following the suggestion given after each one. Write your replies in Spanish. (15 points)

11. You and Catalina are invited to a dance. Accept and ask when it is.

_____

12. You are invited to a baseball game. Decline because you are tired.

_____

13. You are invited to go to a play. Decline because you don't feel like going to the theater.

_____

14. You are invited to go swimming. Decline because you have to study.

_____

15. You are invited to a birthday party. Decline because you have other plans.

_____

SCORE [   ]

TOTAL SCORE [   ] /35

CUMULATIVE SCORE FOR QUIZZES 1–3 [   ] /100

CAPÍTULO 7

¿Qué te gustaría hacer?

I. Listening

Maximum Score: 24 points

A. Janet is having trouble with her Spanish. Listen to the sentences and help her determine the correct completion. Write the letter of the best answer. (14 points)

_____ 1. **a.** maquillarse   **b.** ducharse   **c.** tener prisa

_____ 2. **a.** enfermos   **b.** ocupados   **c.** en la boda

_____ 3. **a.** tener sueño   **b.** tener años   **c.** darse prisa

_____ 4. **a.** dejar un recado   **b.** tener ganas   **c.** maquillarse

_____ 5. **a.** Un momento.   **b.** ¡Cómo no! ¡Ya tengo planes!   **c.** Tal vez otro día.

_____ 6. **a.** centro   **b.** acuario   **c.** parque de atracciones

_____ 7. **a.** Pienso tener sueño.   **b.** ¡Qué lástima!   **c.** Voy al lago.

SCORE _____

B. Cristina is very busy this week. Listen to her half of a telephone conversation with a friend. Then write the letter of the place or event you associate with each activity she mentions, in the order you hear them. (10 points)

a. la boda
b. la casa
c. el zoológico
d. el museo
e. el teatro

8. _____   9. _____   10. _____   11. _____   12. _____

SCORE _____

II. Reading

Maximum Score: 30 points

C. The statements below are parts of phone conversations. Indicate the matching part of each conversation with the correct letter. (10 points)

_____ 13. ¿Puedo hablar con Ricardo, por favor?

_____ 14. Su línea personal está ocupada, señora.

_____ 15. Bueno, Marta. ¿Quieres ir al circo mañana?

_____ 16. ¿Puedo hablar con la señora Salinas?

_____ 17. ¿Te gustaría ir al lago?

a. Claro que sí. ¿A qué hora?
b. Un momento. Lo siento, pero la línea está ocupada.
c. Él no está. ¿Quieres dejar un recado?
d. ¿Puedo dejar un recado?
e. ¡Cómo no! Me gusta mucho nadar y bucear.

SCORE _____

CAPÍTULO 7

Chapter 7 Test

D. Read the phone conversation below and choose the best answer to the questions that follow. (10 points)

ALONSO	Aló. ¿Está Pedro?
JUAN	Lo siento, pero no está. ¿Puedes llamar más tarde?
ALONSO	Sí, pero tengo prisa. ¿Les gustaría a ustedes venir a mi casa en media hora?
JUAN	¿Por qué?
ALONSO	Hay una fiesta de cumpleaños a las nueve. Es una fiesta de sorpresa para María.
JUAN	Pues, no puedo. Ya tengo planes, pero tal vez Pedro pueda ir.
ALONSO	Favor de decirle a Pedro que hay una fiesta.

Pedro returns Alonso's call.

PEDRO	Aló. ¿Alonso?
ALONSO	Sí, soy yo. ¿Qué hay de nuevo?
PEDRO	Juan dice que hay una fiesta esta noche.
ALONSO	Sí, para María. ¿Quieres venir?
PEDRO	¡Cómo no! ¿A qué hora empieza la fiesta?
ALONSO	A las nueve.
PEDRO	Pues, primero tengo que afeitarme.
ALONSO	Está bien. Chao, hasta las nueve.

_____ 18. Alonso is telling Juan about . . .
  a. a party for María
  b. his plans for the weekend

_____ 19. . . . will not be seeing Alonso this evening
  a. Pedro
  b. Juan

_____ 20. Pedro needs to . . .
  a. wash his hair.
  b. shave

_____ 21. Juan and Pedro . . .
  a. are either brothers or close friends
  b. have not met yet

_____ 22. . . . is going to get a big surprise soon.
  a. María
  b. Pedro

SCORE _____

Chapter 7 Test

E. It's Friday evening and Tulio is telling his Aunt Sofía about his plans for tonight. Read their conversation, then mark the statements that follow **a) cierto** or **b) falso**. (10 points)

TÍA SOFÍA ¿Qué piensas hacer esta noche, hijo?
TULIO Meche y yo pensamos cenar primero en el Taco Loco y después vamos a ver una película.
TÍA SOFÍA ¿Y a qué hora debes estar en su casa?
TULIO No voy a su casa. Ella viene aquí con sus padres a las siete y cuarto porque ellos pasan por aquí cuando van a la reunión de la familia Perea.
TÍA SOFÍA ¿A las siete y cuarto? Pero hijo, ya son las siete. ¿Estás listo?
TULIO No, todavía necesito peinarme.
TÍA SOFÍA ¿No vas a ducharte primero?
TULIO Bueno, sí, tía. Creo que debo ducharme.
TÍA SOFÍA Entonces, ¡date prisa, hombre! Ya es tarde.
TULIO Ah, y tía Sofía, ¿me puede planchar la ropa rápidamente, por favor?
TÍA SOFÍA ¡Plancharte la ropa! ¿En quince minutos? No, hijo, lo siento, pero no puedo... ¡Yo también tengo mis planes para esta noche!

_____ 23. Tulio y Meche van al cine esta noche.

_____ 24. Tulio tiene que estar listo en una hora.

_____ 25. La tía Sofía no tiene nada que hacer esta noche.

_____ 26. Tulio necesita ducharse y peinarse.

_____ 27. La tía Sofía va a planchar la ropa de Tulio.

SCORE [ ]

III. Culture

Maximum Score: 4 points

F. Read the statements below. Based on the information in your textbook, determine whether the statements are **a) cierto** or **b) falso**. (4 points)

_____ 28. Having a driver's license at age 16 is common in Latin American countries, as it is in the United States.

_____ 29. Boys in many Spanish-speaking countries typically pay when going out on dates with girls.

SCORE [ ]

CAPÍTULO 7

Chapter 7 Test

IV. Writing

G. Using the cues below, write two sentences in Spanish for each picture. In the first sentence, say the person is not yet ready. In the second sentence, say what the person has to do to get ready. (15 points)

30. Ella

_____

_____

31. Él

_____

_____

32. Mi hermana mayor

_____

_____

33. Yo

_____

_____

34. Tú

_____

_____

SCORE

CAPÍTULO 7

H. Your friend Carolina just invited you to a party on Saturday, but you already have plans. Write a letter of at least four sentences to Carolina. Thank her for inviting you, turn down the invitation, and explain why you can't go. (11 points)

Queridos amigos
Me complazco mucho en invitarlos a una fiesta que se celebra en mi casa el 11 de noviembre. Las festividades comenzarán a las 9:00 de la noche. La celebración es en honor del cumpleaños de mi querida hermana Clara.
Favor de responder

C A P Í T U L O   7

35. _____

_____

_____

_____

_____

_____

_____

_____

_____

_____

SCORE ☐

Chapter 7 Test

I. Write an eight-line phone dialogue in which your friend calls you to invite you to the movies. Your dialogue should include the following: (16 points)

- Typical telephone greetings.
- You ask how the other is doing.
- Your friend asks you if you would like to go to the movies tonight.
- You ask what movie and at what time.
- Your friend says which movie and at what time. (Think of a movie you would like to see and make up a time.)
- You thank your friend but say that you can't make it because you have a lot to do tonight.
- Your friend says it's a shame and suggests that maybe you can go some other day.
- You both say good-bye.

36.   TÚ _____

37. AMIGO _____

38.   TÚ _____

39. AMIGO _____

40.   TÚ _____

41. AMIGO _____

42.   TÚ _____

43. AMIGO _____

SCORE ☐

TOTAL SCORE ☐ /100

CAPÍTULO 7

CAPÍTULO 7 Chapter Test Score Sheet

Circle the letter that matches the most appropriate answer.

I. Listening
Maximum Score: 24 points

A. (14 points)

1. a b c
2. a b c
3. a b c
4. a b c
5. a b c
6. a b c
7. a b c

SCORE [   ]

B. (10 points)

8. a b c d e
9. a b c d e
10. a b c d e
11. a b c d e
12. a b c d e

SCORE [   ]

II. Reading
Maximum Score: 30 points

C. (10 points)

13. a b c d e
14. a b c d e
15. a b c d e
16. a b c d e
17. a b c d e

SCORE [   ]

D. (10 points)

18. a b
19. a b
20. a b
21. a b
22. a b

SCORE [   ]

E. (10 points)

23. a b
24. a b
25. a b
26. a b
27. a b

SCORE [   ]

III. Culture
Maximum Score: 4 points

F. (4 points)

28. a b
29. a b

SCORE [   ]

CAPÍTULO 7

IV. Writing

G. (15 points)

30. _____
_____

31. _____
_____

32. _____
_____

33. _____
_____

34. _____
_____

SCORE [   ]

H. (11 points)

35. _____
_____
_____
_____
_____
_____
_____
_____
_____

SCORE [   ]

I. (16 points)

36.　　TÚ _____
37. AMIGO _____
38.　　TÚ _____
39. AMIGO _____
40.　　TÚ _____
41. AMIGO _____
42.　　TÚ _____
43. AMIGO _____

SCORE [   ]

TOTAL SCORE [   ] /100

CAPÍTULO 7

Quiz 7-1B Capítulo 7 Primer paso

I. Listening

- A. 1. ¿Te gustaría jugar al voleibol esta tarde?
     2. ¿Quieres estudiar conmigo?
     3. Me gustaría hablar con Claudia. ¿Está en casa?
     4. ¿Te gustaría ir al zoológico?
     5. Lo siento, pero Benito no está.

Quiz 7-2B Capítulo 7 Segundo paso

I. Listening

- A. 1. El señor Martínez necesita afeitarse todos los días.
     2. Juanita no está lista. Todavía debe maquillarse.
     3. Gloria necesita ducharse todas las noches.
     4. El señor Gómez necesita lavarse los dientes.
     5. Luisa va a un baile más tarde; por eso tiene que peinarse.

Quiz 7-3B Capítulo 7 Tercer paso

I. Listening

- A. 1. ¿Tienes ganas de cenar en mi casa esta noche?
     2. ¿Te gustaría ir al partido de béisbol mañana?
     3. ¿Quieres ir a tomar un refresco el sábado?
     4. ¿Tienes que estudiar esta noche?
     5. María quiere ir al concierto. ¿Quieres ir con nosotros?

Answers to Quizzes 7-1A, 7-1B

ANSWERS Quiz 7-1A

A. (8 points: 1 point per item)
1. empiezo
2. viene
3. preferimos
4. empieza
5. vienen
6. prefieren
7. empiezas
8. prefieres

B. (12 points: 1.5 points per item)
9. empieza
10. prefiero
11. vienen
12. empiezan
13. preferimos
14. vienes
15. vengo
16. empezamos

C. (10 points: 2 points per item)
Some answers may vary slightly.
Possible answers:
17. Luisa y yo venimos del parque de atracciones.
18. Mamá y Papá vienen del campo.
19. Tomasito viene del circo.
20. Belén viene de la fiesta de cumpleaños de su amiga.
21. Mis primos vienen del lago.

ANSWERS Quiz 7-1B

I. Listening

A. (10 points: 2 points per item)
1. a
2. a
3. b
4. b
5. b

II. Reading

B. (10 points: 2 points per item)
6. Alfredo invites Silvia to come to his house to watch TV and study.
7. No.
8. Silvia is going to the amusement park with Pilar.
9. Alfredo needs to study for an algebra test.
10. Silvia and Alfredo plan to go to the theater.

III. Writing

C. (10 points: 2 points per item)
Answers will vary. Possible answers:
11. Diga
12. Soy yo, Francisco
13. Puedo hablar con Luisa
14. Quieres dejarle un recado
15. Claro que sí

Spanish 1 ¡Ven conmigo!, Chapter 7

ANSWERS Quiz 7-2A

A. (9 points: 1.5 points per item)
   1. piensas
   2. pensamos
   3. pienso
   4. piensan
   5. piensa
   6. pensamos

B. (7 points: 1 point per item)
   Some answers may vary. Possible answers:
   7. Vas a visitar
   8. vamos a hacer/tener
   9. va a tener
   10. Voy a ir
   11. vamos a ver
   12. va a ir
   13. van a asistir/ir

C. (10 points: 2 points per item)
   14. afeitarme
   15. maquillarse
   16. ducharse
   17. lavarte los dientes
   18. peinarte

D. (9 points: 1.5 points per item)
   19. lavarme
   20. ducharte, ducharse
   21. afeitarse
   22. maquillarse, maquillarte

ANSWERS Quiz 7-2B

I. Listening

A. (10 points: 2 points per item)
   1. b
   2. d
   3. e
   4. a
   5. c

II. Reading

B. (10 points: 2 points per item)
   6. mamá
   7. Calvin
   8. Calvin
   9. Calvin
   10. mamá

III. Writing

C. (10 points: 2 points per item)
   Answers will vary. Possible answers:
   11. Necesito peinarme por la mañana antes de ir al colegio.
   12. Necesito ducharme por la noche después de jugar al béisbol.
   13. Necesita afeitarse por la mañana.
   14. Necesita maquillarse por la noche antes de ir a una fiesta.
   15. Necesita lavarse los dientes por la mañana, por la tarde y por la noche.

IV. Culture

D. (5 points: 2.5 points per item)
   16. a   17. b

CAPÍTULO 7

Answers to Quizzes 7-3A, 7-3B

ANSWERS Quiz 7-3A

A. (7 points: 1 point per item)
1. Te gustaría
2. tengo planes
3. Tal vez
4. lo siento
5. ocupado
6. cita
7. Qué lástima

B. (18 points: 2 points per item)
8. tienen prisa
9. tenemos ganas de
10. tiene que
11. tienen que
12. tengo, sueño
13. tiene que
14. tiene, años
15. tienen ganas de
16. tengo, prisa

C. (10 points: 2 points per item)
17. El profesor tiene ganas de ir al campo, pero tiene que trabajar.
18. Tengo ganas de ver una película, pero tengo que cuidar a mi hermanita.
19. Mis amigos y yo tenemos ganas de comer hamburguesas, pero tenemos que estudiar.
20. Tú tienes ganas de tomar un refresco, pero tienes que organizar tu cuarto.
21. Víctor y Ana tienen ganas de asistir al baile, pero tienen que visitar a sus tíos.

ANSWERS Quiz 7-3B

I. Listening

A. (10 points: 2 points per item)
1. e
2. a
3. d
4. c
5. b

II. Reading

B. (10 points: 2 points per item)
Answers will vary. Possible answers:
6. Severiano invites Monica to a dance on Saturday night.
7. Monica has a lot to do on Saturday.
8. Monica has to vacuum and clean her room.
9. No, but Monica's probably going to be tired and not interested in going out.
10. She suggests that maybe they can go out some other day.

III. Writing

C. (15 points: 3 points per item)
Answers will vary. Possible answers:
11. Sí, cómo no. ¿Cuándo es?
12. Gracias, pero no puedo porque estoy cansado/a.
13. Lo siento, pero no tengo ganas de ir al teatro esta noche.
14. No puedo porque tengo que estudiar.
15. Gracias, pero no puedo. Ya tengo planes.

CAPÍTULO 7

I. Listening

A. 1. Después de jugar al béisbol, Luis debe _____.
    2. Ellos no pueden ir porque no están bien. Creo que están _____.
    3. Mi mamá no tiene mucho tiempo. Pienso que debe _____.
    4. —¡Aló! ¿Está Marcela?
        —No, no está. ¿Quieres _____?
    5. ¿Tienes ganas de ir al concierto conmigo?
    6. Nos gustan mucho los animales. Vamos al _____.
    7. ¿Qué piensas hacer esta tarde?

B. ¡Hola, María! Sí, soy yo [...] ¿Cómo estás? [...] Yo bien, gracias. [...] Gracias, María, pero no puedo ir contigo a ver los nuevos elefantes blancos. [...] Lo siento, pero el viernes tampoco puedo. Voy con mi clase de arte a ver una exposición de arte moderna. [...] ¿Y el sábado? Pues, también estoy ocupada. [...] Sí, se casa mi prima Julia. Voy a estar en la ceremonia, y tengo que estar allí a las doce. [...] Oye, María, espera un momentito. Estoy cuidando a mi hermanito Miguel, y él necesita un sándwich. Miguel, toma. Ahora vete a jugar en el patio, ¿quieres? [...] ¿Hola? Ya estoy aquí. [...] Sí, gracias. Creo que el martes puedo ir contigo para ver esa nueva comedia musical. ¡Qué buena idea!

Answers to Chapter 7 Test

I. Listening Maximum Score: 24 points

A. (14 points: 2 points per item)
1. b
2. a
3. c
4. a
5. c
6. b
7. c

B. (10 points: 2 points per item)
8. c
9. d
10. a
11. b
12. e

II. Reading Maximum Score: 30 points

C. (10 points: 2 points per item)
13. c
14. d
15. a
16. b
17. e

D. (10 points: 2 points per item)
18. a
19. b
20. b
21. a
22. a

E. (10 points: 2 points per item)
23. a
24. b
25. b
26. a
27. b

III. Culture Maximum Score: 4 points

F. (4 points: 2 points per item)
28. b   29. a

IV. Writing Maximum Score: 42 points

G. (15 points: 3 points per item)
Answers will vary. Possible answers:
30. Ella no está lista. Tiene que lavarse los dientes.
31. Él no está listo. Tiene que afeitarse.
32. Mi hermana mayor no está lista. Tiene que maquillarse.
33. Yo no estoy listo. Tengo que ducharme.
34. Tú no estás listo. Tienes que peinarte.

H. (11 points)
Answers will vary. Possible answer:
35. Querida Carolina, Muchas gracias por la invitación. Lo siento mucho, pero no puedo ir a la fiesta. Es que ya tengo planes. Voy a salir con mis amigos.

I. (16 points: 2 points per item)
Dialogues will vary. Possible dialogue:
36. ¿Diga?
37. Hola Pablo, ¿cómo estás?
38. Muy bien, ¿y tú?
39. Bien. Oye, ¿quieres ir al cine conmigo?
40. ¿Qué película y a qué hora?
41. Quiero ver (*película*) a las (*hora*).
42. Lo siento, pero no puedo porque tengo mucho que hacer.
43. ¡Qué lástima! Tal vez otro día. Bueno, hasta luego.

CAPÍTULO 8

Nombre _____ Clase _____ Fecha _____

¡A comer!

Quiz 8-1A

Maximum Score: 35

■ PRIMER PASO

Grammar and Vocabulary

A. It's lunchtime, and Celia and Manuel are talking about food. Complete their conversation with the missing words. Each word will be used once. (10 points)

toronja	papitas	plátano	sopa	fuertes	cereal
	pan tostado	ligeros	almuerzo		queso

CELIA   ¿Qué tienes para el **1.** _____ hoy?

MANUEL   A ver... Pues, un sándwich de jamón y **2.** _____, unas

       3. _____ y una manzana. ¿Y tú?

CELIA   Hoy voy a comprar el almuerzo. Tengo ganas de comer **4.** _____ de pollo

       y una ensalada de frutas con **5.** _____, papaya y **6.** _____.

MANUEL   A mí me gusta la fruta para el desayuno. ¿Y tú? ¿Prefieres los desayunos

       7. _____?

CELIA   No, me gustan más los desayunos **8.** _____. Por ejemplo, me encanta el

       9. _____ con leche. A veces como **10.** _____ con jalea también.

SCORE ☐

B. Some friends are wondering where to go for lunch, since everyone likes different kinds of food. Complete their conversation with the correct indirect object pronouns and the correct form of **encantar** or **gustar**. (16 points)

RAMÓN   Pues, a mí **11.** _____ **12.** _____ la pizza y las hamburguesas.

ELENA   A mí **13.** _____ **14.** _____ la pizza con queso, pero no

       15. _____ **16.** _____ para nada las hamburguesas. Alejo, ¿qué

       prefieres almorzar? ¿A ti **17.** _____ **18.** _____ la pizza?

ALEJO   Sí, **19.** _____ **20.** _____ la comida italiana. Es mi comida

       favorita.

ELENA   ¿Y qué **21.** _____ **22.** _____ comer a Pati?

CAPÍTULO 8

Spanish 1 ¡Ven conmigo!, Chapter 8

Testing Program   **197**

Quiz 8-1A

RAMÓN   Creo que 23. _____ 24. _____ la comida china. Ella es vegetari-

ana, entonces no 25. _____ 26. _____ las hamburguesas.

SCORE [   ]

C. Complete the statements about what everyone does for lunch with the correct form of the verb **almorzar**. (5 points)

27. Los domingos, mis padres y yo _____ con mis abuelos.

28. Típicamente, mis abuelos _____ a las dos o tres de la tarde.

29. Este fin de semana, mi primo Claudio _____ con nosotros.

30. Durante la semana, yo _____ con mis amigos Carlos y Andrea casi siempre.

31. ¿Tú siempre _____ en la cafetería también?

SCORE [   ]

D. Everyone is Luis' family is allergic to something. Complete his statements about what different people can't eat with the correct form of the verb **poder**. (4 points)

32. Mi hermano mayor no _____ comer chocolate.

33. Yo no _____ comer papayas.

34. Mamá y yo no _____ comer crema de maní.

35. Mis primos no _____ tomar leche.

SCORE [   ]

TOTAL SCORE [/35]

CAPÍTULO 8

¡A comer!

■ PRIMER PASO

I. Listening

A. Listen as Luisa and Roberto talk about what they like to eat for breakfast. As they say what they like, place a check mark in the appropriate box. Not everything they mention is listed. (10 points)

	Luisa	Roberto
1. huevos		
2. jugo de naranja		
3. leche		
4. pan tostado		
5. tocino		

SCORE _____

II. Reading

B. Read Bárbara's journal entry about the lunch she and her friends are planning. Then complete the chart that follows by writing foods each person likes, loves, and dislikes in the chart below. (10 points)

¿Qué vamos a comer el sábado? A mí me gustan los sándwiches de jamón y queso. A Catalina le encantan los sándwiches de crema de maní, pero no le gustan para nada los de atún. ¿Y Federico? Pues, a él no le gustan los sándwiches de atún tampoco. Pero le encantan los perros calientes. ¡Yo pienso que los perros calientes son horribles!

A todos nosotros nos encanta la pizza. Pero hay un problema: A Catalina le gusta la pizza de piña. A Federico le gusta la pizza de tocino. ¿Y yo? Pues, a mí me encanta la pizza de queso.

	Likes	Loves	Dislikes
Bárbara	6. _____	7. _____	8. _____
Catalina	9. _____	10. _____	11. _____
Federico	12. _____	13. _____	14. _____
15. All three friends love _____.			

SCORE _____

CAPÍTULO 8

Quiz 8-1 B

III. Writing

C. Write five sentences describing what you normally have for breakfast and lunch: one sentence each for what you eat for breakfast and lunch; one sentence each for what you drink with breakfast and lunch; one sentence naming a food or drink that you especially love. (10 points)

16. _____

17. _____

18. _____

19. _____

20. _____

SCORE [ ]

IV. Culture

D. Based on the information in your book, answer **a) cierto** or **b) falso** to the following statements. (5 points)

_____ 21. In Spanish-speaking countries, a breakfast consisting of a roll, fresh fruit, and hot chocolate would be rather unusual.

_____ 22. Lunch in Spanish-speaking countries is a light meal consisting of soup or a sandwich.

SCORE [ ]

TOTAL SCORE [ ] /35

Spanish 1 ¡Ven conmigo!, Chapter 8

C A P Í T U L O

8

¡A comer!

■ SEGUNDO PASO

Grammar and Vocabulary

A. Complete the statements made by diners at a restaurant with the correct Spanish adjectives. Remember to make the adjectives agree with the nouns they refer to. (8 points)

—Este té está **1.** _____. Quiero un té **2.** _____, por favor.
                  (hot)   *(cold)*

—¡Mmm! Hoy la sopa de legumbres está **3.** _____.
                                           (delicious)

—¡Ay! ¡Qué **4.** _____ y **5.** _____ están las enchiladas! Necesito un vaso de
                    (spicy)   *(salty)*

   agua **6.** _____, por favor.
               (cold)

—Los postres aquí son todos **7.** _____. Me encanta el flan de vainilla. Es muy
                                     (delicious)

   8. _____.
      (sweet)

SCORE [_____]

B. While eating at a restaurant, Isabel and Dolores are talking about different foods. Complete their conversation with the correct form of **ser** or **estar**. (16 points)

ISABEL   En el verano, siempre como ensaladas de frutas. **9.** _____ deliciosas. Me

             encantan las comidas frías cuando hace calor.

DOLORES   Yo prefiero las comidas calientes. Creo que las sopas **10.** _____ muy ricas,

             especialmente la sopa de pollo.

ISABEL   ¿Y cómo **11.** _____ tu sopa hoy?

DOLORES   Pues, **12.** _____ un poco salada. ¿Cómo **13.** _____ los frijoles?

ISABEL   **14.** _____ picantes, pero así me gustan. En general la comida picante

            15. _____ mi favorita. Los frijoles que prepara mi abuela

            16. _____ los más ricos del mundo.

SCORE [_____]

C A P Í T U L O 8

Quiz 8-2A

C. Read each situation, then write a statement or question summarizing it using the Spanish expressions for *to be hungry* or *to be thirsty*. Remember to use the correct form of the verb. (6 points)

17. You skipped breakfast, and it's now almost noon.

    Yo _____.

18. Your friend Samuel just bought three hamburgers for lunch.

    Él _____.

19. Your little sister never drinks her juice at breakfast.

    Ella no _____.

20. You wonder why your friend Susana isn't eating her lunch today.

    Susana, ¿no _____?

21. Estela and Marta just finished going for a run on a hot summer afternoon.

    Ellas _____.

22. You and your friends decide to go for ice cream at the mall.

    Nosotros _____.

SCORE [ ]

TOTAL SCORE [/30]

CAPITULO 8

CAPÍTULO 8

¡A comer!

SEGUNDO PASO

Maximum Score: 30

I. Listening

A. Mario is asking you some questions. Find the logical answer and write the letter of your choice. (10 points)

_____ 1. **a.** Almuerzo a las doce.
b. Un sándwich de crema de maní y jalea.
c. Prefiero tomar agua.

_____ 2. **a.** No tengo sed.
b. Me gusta mucho el queso.
c. Me encanta la limonada.

_____ 3. **a.** Está salada.
b. Está solo.
c. Está en la cocina.

_____ 4. **a.** un postre delicioso
b. un perro caliente con papitas
c. huevos

_____ 5. **a.** Sí, está muy rica.
b. Sí, está frío.
c. Sí, tengo mucha sed.

SCORE [   ]

II. Reading

B. Sonia is describing her brother Rafael's eating habits. Read what she says, then choose the best summary for each statement. (10 points)

_____ 6. Mi hermano mayor come todo el tiempo. Mamá necesita ir al supermercado todos los días.
a. Rafael tiene sed.
b. Rafael tiene mucha hambre.
c. Rafael tiene canas.

_____ 7. A él le encanta la sopa de pollo.
a. La sopa está fría.
b. Es su comida favorita.
c. Piensa que la sopa está salada.

_____ 8. También le gustan mucho los refrescos.
a. Piensa que los refrescos son ricos.
b. El refresco está caliente.
c. El refresco está picante.

Quiz 8-2B

_____ 9. A mi hermano le encanta comer en casa de mi tía Loli, especialmente cuando ella prepara su postre favorito.
   a. El postre no está muy dulce.
   b. Rafael piensa que el postre no está muy bueno hoy.
   c. Los postres de la tía Loli son deliciosos.

_____ 10. Rafael toma dos vasos de agua y un vaso de leche con la cena.
   a. La cena está fría.
   b. Rafael tiene sed.
   c. Rafael tiene sueño.

SCORE ☐

III. Writing

C. At the restaurant, you have been served soup, salad, and tea. The waitperson now wants to know if your food is all right. Write a five-sentence dialogue between you and the waitperson that includes the following: (10 points)

• The waitperson asks you how the soup is.

• You tell him it's salty and cold.

• He asks how the salad is.

• You tell him it's delicious.

• You tell him you don't want a dessert.

11. CAMARERO _____

_____

12.   TÚ _____

_____

13. CAMARERO _____

_____

14.   TÚ _____

_____

15.   TÚ _____

_____

SCORE ☐

TOTAL SCORE ☐ /30

¡A comer!

■ TERCER PASO

Grammar and Vocabulary

A. Complete the statements and requests made by a waitperson and diners at a restaurant with the missing words and expressions. Each expression will be used only once. (9 points)

voy a pedir	Qué le puedo traer	Está incluida	Quisiera
limpia	sucia	vas a pedir	Desea algo más	cuenta

— Buenas tardes, señor. ¿**1.** _____?

— **2.** _____ el bistec con papas fritas.

— Muy bien. ¿**3.** _____?

— Sí, una ensalada de lechuga y tomate.

— Camarero, necesito una servilleta **4.** _____, por favor. Esta servil-

   leta está **5.** _____.

— Ricardo, aquí viene el camarero. ¿Qué **6.** _____?

— Creo que **7.** _____ el pescado.

— Maribel, ¿tienes allí la **8.** _____? ¿Cuánto es?

— Son 34 dólares.

— ¿Es todo? ¿**9.** _____ la propina?   SCORE [   ]

B. Write the Spanish word for the item you would need to do the following things. Include the indefinite article. (7 points)

10. wipe your hands _____

11. slice carrots and tomatoes for a salad _____

12. taste soup or ice cream _____

13. serve lemonade _____

14. eat your sandwich off of _____

15. eat peas or twirl spaghetti _____

16. put your cereal and milk in _____

SCORE [   ]

Quiz 8-3A

C. You're at a restaurant with your nephew Pepito, who is four years old and pretty mischievous. Complete what you say to Pepito and the waiter with the correct form of **otro**. (7 points)

¡Ay, Pepito! Camarero, ¿nos puede traer 17. _____ vaso de leche, por favor? ¡Ay, no! Y también 18. _____ tenedores y 19. _____ cuchara. Y ahora, ¿qué? Camarero, ¿nos trae también 20. _____ servilletas y 21. _____ ensalada? Pepito, mira a los 22. _____ niños aquí. Ellos son buenos y no hacen esas cosas malas. Y aquí viene el camarero con 23. _____ postre para ti. Por favor, sé (be) bueno.

SCORE [   ]

D. For a health class project, you polled students on what they ate. Now explain how many of the following items are consumed by your classmates in a year, using the data from the poll below. Write all numbers as words. (12 points)

plátanos	842	bistecs	591
uvas	36.740	sándwiches	11.913
ensaladas	655	refrescos	4.831
papitas	168.311	batidos	2.147

En un año, los estudiantes de mi colegio comen...

24. _____ plátanos.

25. _____ uvas.

26. _____ ensaladas.

27. _____ papitas.

28. _____ bistecs.

29. _____ sándwiches.

Ellos toman...

30. _____ refrescos.

31. _____ batidos.

SCORE [   ]

TOTAL SCORE [   ] /35

Spanish 1 ¡Ven conmigo!, Chapter 8

CAPÍTULO 8

¡A comer!

Quiz 8-3B

■ TERCER PASO

Maximum Score: 35

I. Listening

A. Rosita is working as a waitress in a restaurant. The people at the table she's waiting on right now want to know the prices of various items. As Rosita answers, write the price for each item. (10 points)

COMIDA	PRECIO

1. _____ pesos

2. _____ pesos

3. _____ pesos

4. _____ pesos

5. _____ pesos   SCORE [   ]

II. Reading

B. The restaurant you're in is so noisy that you and the waitperson keep hearing what's said at other tables. Show what you and the waitperson really say to each other by choosing the right letter. (10 points)

_____ **6.** ¿Qué le puedo traer?
    a. Primero quisiera la ensalada de fruta.
    b. Es aparte. No está incluida.

_____ **7.** Camarera, hay una mosca *(fly)* en el té.
    ¿Me trae otro vaso, por favor?
    a. ¡Claro que sí!
    b. ¿Cuánto es?

_____ **8.** ¿Qué legumbre quiere usted?
    a. La cuenta, por favor.
    b. El maíz, por favor.

Spanish 1 ¡Ven conmigo!, Chapter 8

Testing Program **207**

Quiz 8-3B

_____ 9. ¿Desea usted algo más?
     a. ¿Es aparte la propina?
     b. Quisiera un postre, por favor.

_____ 10. La cuenta, por favor.
     a. Muy bien. La propina está incluida.
     b. Prefiero la sopa del día.

SCORE _____

III. Writing

C. The waitperson is taking your order. Write five sentences to complete the following. (10 points)

CAMARERA ¿Qué le puedo traer?

11.   TÚ _____

CAMARERA ¿Y qué legumbres quiere usted?

12.   TÚ _____

CAMARERA ¿Quiere usted una ensalada?

13.   TÚ _____

CAMARERA Y para tomar, ¿prefiere usted té o un refresco?

14.   TÚ _____

CAMARERA ¿Algo más?

15.   TÚ _____

SCORE _____

IV. Culture

D. Based on the information in your book, answer **a) cierto** or **b) falso** to the following statements. (5 points)

_____ 16. Many people in Spanish-speaking countries do not switch the fork to the right hand after cutting food.

_____ 17. In Spain, a **tortilla** is made from cormeal or flour, pressed into a flat shape and cooked on a griddle.

SCORE _____

TOTAL SCORE _____ /35

CUMULATIVE SCORE FOR QUIZZES 1–3 _____ /100

CAPÍTULO 8

¡A comer!

I. Listening

Maximum Score: 30 points

A. Listen as a group of friends talk about what they want for lunch. Match each person with what he or she says. (8 points)

Victoria   Héctor   Lupe   Sebastián

1. _____   **a.** Lupe

2. _____   **b.** Sebastián

3. _____   **c.** Victoria

4. _____   **d.** Héctor

SCORE [   ]

B. Carmiña and Miguel have gone to a restaurant for dinner. Listen to the conversation between them and their waiter. Then indicate what each of them had to eat by putting **a)** for **Carmiña**, **b)** for **Miguel**, or **c)** for **neither** next to the food item. (22 points)

_____ **5.** arroz con pollo   _____ **10.** helado de chocolate

_____ **6.** pastel   _____ **11.** leche

_____ **7.** café   _____ **12.** té frío

_____ **8.** carne de res   _____ **13.** un sándwich

_____ **9.** flan   _____ **14.** camarones

        _____ **15.** sopa

SCORE [   ]

CAPÍTULO 8

Chapter 8 Test

II. Reading

C. Carlos is writing about his trip to a restaurant. Read his story and answer the questions which follow it. (10 points)

> Hoy estamos en el restaurante "La Margarita". Son las doce y media y estoy con mis amigos José, Carmen, Luisa y Juan Luis. Nos gusta mucho salir a comer en los restaurantes de la ciudad. Carmen dice que la comida aquí siempre es muy rica. Hoy tienen muchos platos deliciosos. Hay también una camarera muy amable. La mesa es muy grande y está cerca de la puerta. A mí me encanta la comida aquí.
>
> La camarera nos trae el menú y nos pregunta qué vamos a pedir. Las chicas quieren una ensalada de frutas porque hace mucho calor. La ensalada tiene uvas, toronjas y naranjas. ¡Qué rica! Juan Luis pide jamón con legumbres y José pide sopa de cebolla. Yo quiero la carne de res con arroz y maíz. De postre las chicas y José no quieren nada, pero yo como pastel de chocolate y a Juan Luis le gusta el flan. Después del postre, tomamos café, pagamos la cuenta y salimos a pasear.

_____ **16.** Los chicos tienen una mesa para...
  a. desayunar
  b. almorzar
  c. cenar

_____ **17.** La comida del restaurante es muy...
  a. buena
  b. mala
  c. salada

_____ **18.** Las chicas prefieren algo...
  a. ligero
  b. caliente
  c. picante

_____ **19.** De postre, Carlos pide...
  a. pastel
  b. flan
  c. café

_____ **20.** Los chicos toman... antes de pagar la cuenta.
  a. café
  b. té
  c. refrescos

SCORE [   ]

D. Read the following ad for **Fonda del Mar**. Then answer the questions that follow. (6 points)

> ## Fonda del Mar
>
> ### Pescado y mariscos° para usted y para toda su familia. Los preparamos frescos todos los días.
>
> **Escuche lo que dicen nuestros clientes:**
>
> Carlota Méndez: En Fonda del Mar la comida está riquísima. Se sirven excelentes mariscos: camarones, langostas, mejillas, almejas y ostras. Y los sirven rápido y calientes como en su casa.
>
> Paco Cárdenas: En otros restaurantes los mariscos salen muy salados. En Fonda del Mar, los cocineros preparan platos riquísimos. Siempre están perfectos los mariscos y nunca salados.
>
> María Saavedra: A mí me encanta la comida picante. En Fonda del Mar tienen platos especiales para mí. Si a usted le gusta la comida picante, ¡venga a comer en Fonda del Mar!
>
> Carlitos Saavedra: De postre, me encanta el flan.
>
> **Fonda del Mar**
> **19402 Avenida de la Iglesia**
> **tel: 534-92-95**

°**mariscos** *shellfish*

_____ 21. What is **Fonda del Mar**?
  a. a restaurant supply store
  b. a wholesale seafood store
  c. a restaurant

_____ 22. What does Paco Cárdenas give as his main complaint about shellfish at some restaurants?
  a. They're too hot.
  b. They're too cold.
  c. They're too salty.

_____ 23. What kind of food does María Saavedra like?
  a. spicy food
  b. cold food
  c. salads

SCORE [   ]

C A P Í T U L O 8

Chapter 8 Test

E. Carlos and Adela are eating out. Read their conversation, then indicate if each statement is **a) cierto** or **b) falso**. (14 points)

ADELA	Quisiera los camarones con arroz, por favor.
CARLOS	No tengo mucha hambre. Por lo general no almuerzo, y quiero algo ligero.
CAMARERO	Pues, señor, aquí tenemos unas ensaladas muy buenas. La ensalada de la casa lleva lechuga, tomate, cebolla, zanahoria, queso y atún. ¿Le puedo traer una?
CARLOS	Sí, me trae una, por favor. ¡Qué rico! Y de tomar, un agua mineral.
CAMARERO	¿Y usted, señorita? ¿Qué desea para beber?
ADELA	No tengo mucha sed, pero sí tengo frío. ¿Me puede traer un té caliente, por favor?
CAMARERO	¿Algo más?
CARLOS	Sí... esta cuchara está sucia.
CAMARERO	Ahora mismo le traigo una limpia.

(Veinte minutos después)

CAMARERO	¿Qué desean de postre?
ADELA	Para mí, helado de fresa, y después café.
CARLOS	Para mí, un flan. Y me trae también la cuenta, por favor.

_____ 24. Adela doesn't like seafood.

_____ 25. Carlos usually has a light lunch.

_____ 26. Carlos likes salads.

_____ 27. Adela feels a little chilly.

_____ 28. Carlos asks for a clean knife.

_____ 29. Adela likes fruit desserts.

_____ 30. The friends are going to split the bill.

SCORE [ ]

III. Culture

Maximum Score: 8 points

F. Read the statements below. Based on the information in your textbook, determine whether the statements are **a) cierto** or **b) falso**. (8 points)

_____ 31. Spaniards brought turkey and chocolate to the Americas when they came.

_____ 32. Most Ecuadorean food is not very spicy.

_____ 33. **Una merienda** is a heavy meal eaten around 8:00 P.M.

_____ 34. The "typical dish" in Spain and Latin America varies from country to country.

SCORE [ ]

Spanish 1 ¡Ven conmigo!, Chapter 8

CAPÍTULO 8

IV. Writing

Maximum Score: 32 points

G. Write a conversation between the waiter and Carolina in which you include the following: (12 points)

- The waiter asks Carolina how the soup is.

- Carolina says she doesn't like the soup at all.

- The waiter asks Carolina why she doesn't like the soup.

- Carolina says that the soup is cold and salty.

- The waiter asks if he can bring her anything else.

- Carolina says no thank you and asks for the bill.

35. CAMARERO _____

_____

36. CAROLINA _____

_____

37. CAMARERO _____

_____

38. CAROLINA _____

_____

39. CAMARERO _____

_____

40. CAROLINA _____

_____

SCORE ☐

CAPÍTULO 8

Chapter 8 Test

H. Describe your favorite meal of the day. Explain what foods you like to eat and what you like about each one. (10 points)

41. _____

_____

_____

_____

_____

_____

SCORE [   ]

I. You and your friend have just finished eating in a restaurant. You now need to pay the bill in **pesos**. Write five sentences in Spanish for the following situation. (10 points)

a. Your friend asks for the bill.

b. You ask your friend how much the bill is.

c. Your friend says it's 6.550 **pesos.** (Write the number as words.)

d. You ask if the tip is included.

e. Your friend says it's separate. It's 980 **pesos.** (Write the number as words.)

42. TU AMIGO _____

_____

43. TÚ _____

_____

44. TU AMIGO _____

_____

45. TÚ _____

_____

46. TU AMIGO _____

_____

SCORE [   ]

TOTAL SCORE [   ] /100

Spanish 1 ¡Ven conmigo!, Chapter 8

Nombre _____ Clase _____ Fecha _____

CAPÍTULO 8 Chapter Test Score Sheet

Circle the letter that matches the most appropriate response.

I. Listening
Maximum Score: 30 points

A. (8 points)

1. a b c d
2. a b c d
3. a b c d
4. a b c d

SCORE [____]

B. (22 points)

5. a b c
6. a b c
7. a b c
8. a b c
9. a b c

10. a b c
11. a b c
12. a b c
13. a b c
14. a b c
15. a b c

SCORE [____]

II. Reading
Maximum Score: 30 points

C. (10 points)

16. a b c
17. a b c
18. a b c
19. a b c
20. a b c

SCORE [____]

D. (6 points)

21. a b c
22. a b c
23. a b c

SCORE [____]

E. (14 points)

24. a b
25. a b
26. a b
27. a b
28. a b
29. a b
30. a b

SCORE [____]

III. Culture
Maximum Score: 10 points

F. (8 points)

31. a b
32. a b
33. a b
34. a b

SCORE [____]

C A P Í T U L O   8

IV. Writing

Maximum Score: 32 points

G. (12 points)

35. CAMARERO _____

_____

36. CAROLINA _____

_____

37. CAMARERO _____

_____

38. CAROLINA _____

_____

39. CAMARERO _____

_____

40. CAROLINA _____

_____

SCORE ☐

H. (10 points)

41. _____

_____

_____

_____

_____

_____

SCORE ☐

I. (10 points)

42. _____

43. _____

44. _____

45. _____

46. _____

SCORE ☐

TOTAL SCORE ☐ /100

Spanish 1 ¡Ven conmigo!, Chapter 8

Quiz 8-1B Capítulo 8 Primer paso

I. Listening

    A.   LUISA   Roberto, ¿qué te gusta para el desayuno?

    ROBERTO   Me encantan los huevos con tocino. ¿Y a ti?

    LUISA   A mí me gusta el pan tostado o el pan dulce y para beber, me gusta la leche. Y tú, ¿qué prefieres tomar?

    ROBERTO   Prefiero el jugo de naranja. También me gustan mucho las frutas, especialmente las toronjas.

Quiz 8-2B Capítulo 8 Segundo paso

I. Listening

    A.   1. ¿Qué comes cuando tienes hambre?

        2. ¿Qué tomas cuando tienes sed?

        3. ¿Cómo está la sopa hoy?

        4. ¿Qué hay para el desayuno?

        5. La ensalada está deliciosa, ¿no?

Quiz 8-3B Capítulo 8 Tercer paso

I. Listening

    A.   CLIENTE 1   ¿Cuánto son los batidos?

    ROSITA   Son dos mil pesos cada uno.

    CLIENTE 2   ¿Y la sopa? ¿Cuánto es?

    ROSITA   La sopa es tres mil ochocientos pesos.

    CLIENTE 3   Quisiera saber cuánto es el bistec.

    ROSITA   El bistec cuesta once mil doscientos cincuenta pesos.

    CLIENTE 4   ¿Y cuánto es la ensalada?

    ROSITA   ¿La ensalada? A ver. La ensalada es cuatro mil pesos.

    CLIENTE 5   Dígame, por favor, ¿cuánto es el pollo?

    ROSITA   El pollo es nueve mil seiscientos pesos.

ANSWERS Quiz 8-1A

A. (10 points: 1 point per item)
1. almuerzo
2. queso
3. papitas
4. sopa
5. plátano/toronja
6. toronja/plátano
7. fuertes
8. ligeros
9. cereal
10. pan tostado

B. (16 points: 1 point per item)
11. me
12. encantan/gustan
13. me
14. encanta/gusta
15. me
16. gustan
17. te
18. gusta
19. me
20. encanta/gusta
21. le
22. gusta
23. le
24. encanta/gusta
25. le
26. gustan

C. (5 points: 1 point per item)
27. almorzamos
28. almuerzan
29. almuerza
30. almuerzo
31. almuerzas

D. (4 points: 1 point per item)
32. puede
33. puedo
34. podemos
35. pueden

ANSWERS Quiz 8-1B

I. Listening

A. (10 points: 2 points per item)

	Luisa	Roberto
1. huevos		✔
2. jugo de naranja		✔
3. leche	✔	
4. pan tostado	✔	
5. tocino		✔

II. Reading

B. (10 points: 1 point per item)
6. sándwiches de jamón y queso
7. pizza de queso
8. perros calientes
9. pizza de piña
10. sándwiches de crema de maní
11. sándwiches de atún
12. pizza de tocino
13. perros calientes
14. sándwiches de atún
15. pizza

III. Writing

C. (10 points: 2 points per item)
Answers will vary. Possible answers:
16. Para el desayuno como cereal con leche.
17. Para el almuerzo como un sándwich y papitas.
18. Para el desayuno tomo un vaso de jugo.
19. Para el almuerzo tomo un vaso de leche.
20. Me encanta el tocino.

IV. Culture

D. (5 points: 2.5 points per item)
21. b
22. b

Spanish 1 ¡Ven conmigo!, Chapter 8

Answers to Quizzes 8-2A, 8-2B

ANSWERS Quiz 8-2A

A. (8 points: 1 point per item)
1. caliente
2. frío
3. rica/deliciosa
4. picantes
5. saladas
6. fría
7. ricos/deliciosos
8. dulce

B. (16 points: 2 points per item)
9. Son
10. son
11. está
12. está
13. están
14. Están
15. es
16. son

C. (6 points: 1 point per item)
17. tengo (mucha) hambre
18. tiene (mucha) hambre
19. tiene (mucha) sed
20. tienes hambre
21. tienen (mucha) sed
22. tenemos (mucha) hambre

ANSWERS Quiz 8-2B

I. Listening

A. (10 points: 2 points per item)
1. b
2. c
3. a
4. c
5. a

II. Reading

B. (10 points: 2 points per item)
6. b
7. b
8. a
9. c
10. b

III. Writing

C. (10 points: 2 points per item)
Answers will vary. Possible answers:
11. Buenas tardes. ¿Cómo está la sopa?
12. Está un poco salada y fría.
13. ¿Cómo está la ensalada?
14. Está deliciosa.
15. No me gustaría nada de postre.

CAPÍTULO 8

ANSWERS Quiz 8-3A

A. (9 points: 1 point per item)
1. Qué le puedo traer
2. Quisiera
3. Desea algo más
4. limpia
5. sucia
6. vas a pedir
7. voy a pedir
8. cuenta
9. Está incluida

B. (7 points: 1 point per item)
Some answers may vary. Possible answers:
10. una servilleta
11. un cuchillo
12. una cuchara
13. un vaso
14. un plato
15. un tenedor
16. un plato hondo/un tazón

C. (7 points: 1 point per item)
17. otro
18. otros
19. otra
20. otras
21. otra
22. otros
23. otro

D. (12 points: 1.5 points per item)
24. ochocientos cuarenta y dos
25. treinta y seis mil, setecientas cuarenta
26. seiscientas cincuenta y cinco
27. ciento setenta y ocho mil, trescientas once
28. quinientos noventa y un
29. once mil, novecientos trece
30. cuatro mil, ochocientos treinta y un
31. dos mil, ciento cuarenta y siete

ANSWERS Quiz 8-3B

I. Listening

A. (10 points: 2 points per item)
1. 2.000
2. 3.800
3. 11.250
4. 4.000
5. 9.600

II. Reading

B. (10 points: 2 points per item)
6. a
7. a
8. b
9. b
10. a

III. Writing

C. (10 points: 2 points per item)
Answers will vary. Possible answers:
11. ¿Me puede traer el arroz con pollo, por favor?
12. Quisiera las zanahorias.
13. No, gracias.
14. Prefiero tomar un refresco.
15. ¿Me puede traer un poco de pan, por favor?

IV. Culture

D. (5 points: 2.5 points per item)
16. a
17. b

I. Listening

A.
1. LUPE   Me encantan el arroz con pollo y las legumbres.
2. VICTORIA   De almuerzo quiero un sándwich de crema de maní y jalea. También quisiera una manzana.
3. HÉCTOR   Para mí un perro caliente, papitas y un vaso de té frío.
4. SEBASTIÁN   Para el almuerzo me gustaría tomar una sopa, con un sándwich y un vaso de leche descremada.

B. CARMIÑA   Muy bien. Creo que voy a pedir la sopa primero. Luego ¿me trae el arroz con pollo, por favor? Y para beber quisiera un vaso de leche.

CAMARERO   ¿Y para usted señor?

MIGUEL   Yo quiero un sándwich de jamón y queso. Póngame por favor mostaza, lechuga y tomate.

CAMARERO   Muy bien, señor. ¿Y qué desea para tomar?

MIGUEL   Para tomar, una taza de café por favor.

CAMARERO   ¿Desean postre?

MIGUEL   Sí. De postre, quisiera un flan, por favor.

CARMIÑA   Para mí, el helado de chocolate.

I. Listening Maximum Score: 30 points

A. (8 points: 2 points per item)
1. a
2. c
3. d
4. b

B. (22 points: 2 points per item)
5. a
6. c
7. b
8. c
9. b
10. a
11. a
12. c
13. b
14. c
15. a

II. Reading Maximum Score: 30 points

C. (10 points: 2 points per item)
16. b
17. a
18. a
19. a
20. a

D. (6 points: 2 points per item)
21. c
22. c
23. a

E. (14 points: 2 points per item)
24. b
25. b
26. a
27. a
28. b
29. a
30. b

III. Culture Maximum Score: 10 points

F. (8 points: 2 points per item)
31. b
32. a
33. b
34. a

IV. Writing Maximum Score: 32 points

G. (12 points: 2 points per item)
Answers will vary. Possible answers:
35. ¿Cómo está la sopa?
36. ¡Ay! No me gusta la sopa para nada.
37. ¿Por qué no le gusta?
38. Está fría y salada.
39. ¿Le puedo traer algo más?
40. No, gracias. ¿Me trae la cuenta, por favor?

H. (10 points)
Answers will vary. Possible answer:
41. Mi comida favorita es el desayuno. Me gusta mucho comer huevos y tocino. Me gusta el tocino porque es muy salado. Me gustan los huevos porque son ricos. Para tomar, me gusta el jugo de naranja porque es muy dulce.

I. (10 points: 2 points per item)
Answers will vary. Possible answers:
42. La cuenta, por favor.
43. ¿Cuánto es?
44. Seis mil quinientos cincuenta pesos.
45. ¿Está incluida la propina?
46. Es aparte. La propina es novecientos ochenta pesos.

CAPÍTULO 8

Spanish 1 ¡Ven conmigo!, Chapter 8

Nombre _____ Clase _____ Fecha _____

¡Vamos de compras!

Quiz 9-1A

■ PRIMER PASO

Maximum Score: 30

Grammar and Vocabulary

A. Read the statements about what people need to buy and which stores they need to visit, then complete each one with the correct missing word. (10 points)

juguetes	flores	zapatería	dulcería	tarjeta	joyería
corbata	tienda de comestibles			aretes	pastelería

1. Busco un collar para mi hermana. Voy a la _____ hoy.

2. Hijos, vamos a la _____ esta tarde. Necesitamos pan, leche y fruta.

3. Quiero comprarle unas _____ a mamá. Voy a la florería mañana.

4. Papá necesita una _____ nueva. ¿Quieres ir conmigo al almacén más tarde?

5. Pienso ir a la _____ para comprar el regalo de abuela. A ella le encanta el chocolate.

6. Buscas unos _____ para Chela, ¿verdad? Si quieres, voy contigo a la juguetería este fin de semana.

7. Para el regalo de mi prima, necesito ir a la joyería. Voy a comprarle unos _____.

8. Quiero comprarle una _____ cómica a Gabriela. ¿Tienes ganas de ir conmigo a la papelería?

9. Mamá, necesito unos zapatos para ir al baile. ¿Puedo ir a la _____ esta tarde?

10. Tengo ganas de comer algo dulce, como unas galletas o un pastel de manzana. Pienso ir a la _____ después de clases.

SCORE [ ]

B. Complete the statements about what you are going to give people on their birthdays with the correct indirect object pronoun. (6 points)

11. A mi primo _____ voy a regalar una novela.

12. A mi padre _____ voy a regalar una planta.

13. A ti _____ voy a regalar un disco compacto.

14. A mis hermanas _____ voy a regalar unos dulces.

15. Isa y Luis, a ustedes _____ voy a regalar unos carteles.

16. Mamá, a ti _____ voy a regalar unos aretes.

SCORE [ ]

Spanish 1 ¡Ven conmigo!, Chapter 9

Testing Program **223**

Quiz 9-1A

Now explain what people are going to give you and your friends for your next birthdays by completing the statements with the correct indirect object pronoun. (6 points)

17. Mis padres _____ van a regalar unas zapatillas de tenis.

18. A Rubén y a mí _____ van a regalar unas camisetas.

19. Mi hermano _____ va a regalar unas revistas.

20. A Teresa y a mí _____ van a regalar una radio.

21. Mi abuelo _____ va a regalar un libro.

22. Y a mi hermano y a mí _____ va a regalar un juego de mesa.   SCORE ☐

C. Look at the map of downtown, then complete the directions by underlining the correct expressions. (8 points)

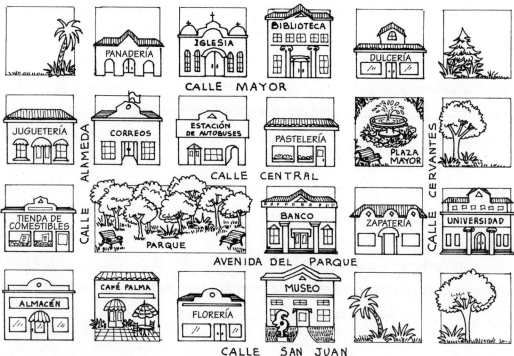

23. La florería queda (al lado del/encima del) museo.
24. La juguetería está (a dos cuadras del/lejos del) almacén.
25. La panadería queda a tres cuadras del (café/museo).
26. La zapatería queda (debajo de/a dos cuadras de) la dulcería.
27. La dulcería está (lejos de/encima de) la tienda de comestibles.
28. La pastelería queda (cerca del/a tres cuadras del) parque.
29. Correos y la juguetería quedan al lado del (parque/almacén).
30. La tienda de comestibles está (cerca de/lejos de) la universidad.   SCORE ☐

TOTAL SCORE ☐ /30

CAPÍTULO 9

¡Vamos de compras!

■ PRIMER PASO

Maximum Score: 30

I. Listening

A. Listen as Juanita tells her friend Carola what presents she plans to give her family members. Choose the store that she needs to go to in order to purchase each gift. Write the letter of the store beside the name of the person. (10 points)

_____ 1. Mamá

_____ 2. Su hermana

_____ 3. Su abuela

_____ 4. Paco

_____ 5. Papá

FLORERIA

Juguetes

ZAPATERIA

JOYERIA MENDEZ

ALMACEN

a.   b.   c.   d.   e.

SCORE [   ]

II. Reading

B. Everyone in the Villarreal family is looking for a birthday present for someone. They've just moved, so they're not sure where to go. Read their statements and questions and choose the correct response to each. (6 points)

_____ 6. Tengo que comprar un collar.

_____ 7. ¿Dónde está la pastelería?

_____ 8. A mi madre le gusta escuchar música clásica.

_____ 9. ¿Para quién es el regalo?

_____ 10. ¿Me puede decir dónde puedo comprar un juego de mesa para Arturo?

_____ 11. Prefiero regalarle una planta a mi abuela.

a. Es para mi padre. Es una corbata.
b. Está al lado de la dulcería.
c. Debes ir a la florería que está a dos cuadras de aquí.
d. En la zapatería cerca del almacén.
e. Necesitas ir a la joyería.
f. En la Juguetería García. Está cerca de la panadería.
g. Pues, debes comprarle un disco compacto.

SCORE [   ]

Quiz 9-1B

III. Writing

C. Using the cues, write a sentence in Spanish saying what the first person plans to give to the second person. (10 points)

12. My parents/my sister/earrings _____

_____

13. I/my father/wallet _____

_____

14. My grandfather/my brothers and sisters/T-shirts _____

_____

15. My father/my mother/necklace _____

_____

16. My older brother/my younger brother/toys _____

_____

SCORE [   ]

IV. Culture

D. Based on the information in your book, respond with **a) cierto** or **b) falso** to the following statements. (4 points)

_____ 17. It is not uncommon for people in Spanish-speaking countries to go grocery shopping every day.

_____ 18. Spanish-speakers usually go only to large supermarkets instead of small specialty stores when shopping for food.

SCORE [   ]

TOTAL SCORE [   ] /30

Nombre _____ Clase _____ Fecha _____

9 ¡Vamos de compras!

Quiz 9-2A

Maximum Score: 35

■ SEGUNDO PASO

Grammar and Vocabulary

A. What does everyone want to buy at the clothing store? Write the correct Spanish word for the items pictured. Include the indefinite articles. (10 points)

1. _____

2. _____

3. _____

4. _____

5. _____

6. _____

7. _____

8. _____

9. _____

10. _____

SCORE ☐

B. Tell your friend Elena about the unusual clothing you found at a thrift store. Write the Spanish expressions for the items below. (6 points)

11. a plaid jacket _____

12. some striped socks _____

13. an orange suit _____

14. a purple belt _____

SCORE ☐

Quiz 9-2A

C. You work in a department store. Tell customers what the items below are made of. Choose a logical material for each item and use the correct expression with **ser**. (9 points)

cuero	algodón
lana	seda

15. corbata _____

16. suéteres de esquí _____

17. cartera _____

18. camisetas para niños _____

19. botas _____

20. calcetines de tenis _____

SCORE [   ]

D. Read what Celia says about two local stores, Almacenes Rivas and Boutique Jazz. Then make comparisons between the two stores, based on what you've read and using the correct form of the adjectives in parentheses. (10 points)

Almacenes Rivas	Boutique Jazz
Es enorme. Tienen mucha ropa.	No tienen mucha ropa allí.
Los precios son altos.	Los precios son bajos.
Me gustan las personas que trabajan allí.	¡Uf! ¡Qué antipáticos son todos!
La ropa formal allí es muy elegante.	También es muy elegante su ropa formal.
Está muy lejos de mi casa.	Está al lado de mi casa.

21. el almacén/el boutique (grande)

_____

22. la ropa en Rivas/la ropa en Jazz (caro)

_____

23. las personas que trabajan en el almacén/las personas que trabajan en el boutique (simpático)

_____

24. la ropa formal en el almacén/la ropa formal en el boutique (elegante)

_____

25. el almacén/el boutique (cerca)

_____

SCORE [   ]

TOTAL SCORE [/35]

CAPÍTULO 9

9 ¡Vamos de compras!

Quiz 9-2B

■ SEGUNDO PASO

Maximum Score: 35

I. Listening

A. You and Rosa are at a come-as-you-are party, and she keeps talking about people you don't know. You ask her to identify each one by describing what each person is wearing. Write the letter of the person being described. (10 points)

a.

b.

c.

d.

e.

1. _____   2. _____   3. _____   4. _____   5. _____   SCORE [   ]

II. Reading

B. Read how various people respond to the questions about their clothing when asked by Rodolfo. If their answers are logical, write **sí**. If not, write **no**. (12 points)

_____ 6. ¿Qué ropa llevas cuando hace calor?
        Llevo una chaqueta de lana o un suéter.

_____ 7. ¿Qué ropa llevas cuando vas a un baile formal?
        Llevo un vestido de seda y zapatos bonitos.

_____ 8. ¿Qué ropa llevas en el invierno cuando hace frío?
        Prefiero llevar botas y una chaqueta de lana.

_____ 9. ¿Qué llevas cuando trabajas en la oficina?
        Llevo un traje de baño y sandalias.

_____ 10. ¿Qué ropa llevas para ir a la piscina?
        En general, llevo una corbata de rayas, una camisa de algodón y un cinturón de cuero.

_____ 11. ¿Qué llevas cuando vas al colegio?
        Llevo unos pantalones, una camisa o una camiseta y zapatos.   SCORE [   ]

Quiz 9-2B

III. Writing

C. For each picture, write a sentence in Spanish comparing the two items. Choose from the following adjectives in your comparisons: **caro, cómodo, formal, barato, feo**. Be sure to write complete sentences. (9 points)

12. _____
    _____
    _____

13. _____
    _____
    _____

14. _____
    _____
    _____

SCORE [____]

IV. Culture

D. Based on the information in your textbook, answer **a) cierto** or **b) falso** to the following statements. (4 points)

_____ 15. To Spanish-speaking teens, it's very important to have a lot of clothes, instead of fewer items of clothing of better quality.

_____ 16. Fashions which are popular in the U.S. are also likely to be in style in Spain and Latin America.

SCORE [____]

TOTAL SCORE [____] /35

Nombre _____ Clase _____ Fecha _____

¡Vamos de compras!

Quiz 9-3A

■ TERCER PASO

Maximum Score: 35

Grammar and Vocabulary

A. Complete these statements made by shoppers at a department store with the correct Spanish forms of the demonstrative adjectives. (15 points)

—Mira... me gusta 1. _____ falda. Pero 2. _____ pantalones
　　　　　　　　　　　　　　　　(this)　　　　　　　　　　　　　　　　　　*(those)*

son horribles.

—Voy a comprar 3. _____ cinturón, pero no quiero 4. _____
　　　　　　　　　　　　　　(this)　　　　　　　　　　　　　　　　　　　　　*(those)*

corbatas. Pienso comprar 5. _____ camisa también.
　　　　　　　　　　　　　　　　　(that)

—6. _____ vestido es muy bonito, ¿no? Y me gustan mucho
　　　(That)

7. _____ blusas blancas.
　　　(these)

—¿Qué compro para ir a la playa? Me gustan 8. _____ traje de baño y
　　　　　　　　　　　　　　　　　　　　　　　　　　　　　　(this)

9. _____ camisetas. Y me encantan 10. _____ sandalias allí.
　　(these)　　　　　　　　　　　　　　　　　　　　　　　*(those)*

SCORE _____

B. Mariana and her friends are window-shopping. Use **cuesta** or **cuestan** to complete what they say about the prices of the things they see. (6 points)

11. ¿Ves esos bluejeans allí? ¿Cuánto _____?

12. Me gusta mucho esa chaqueta. ¿Cuánto _____?

13. ¡Mira! ¡Ese vestido _____ 400 dólares!

14. Necesito unas camisetas, pero aquí _____ 30 dólares. Es mucho, ¿no?

15. Esos zapatos son muy elegantes, ¿no? ¿Cuánto _____?

16. Esa blusa de seda _____ 60 dólares. Es cara, pero me gusta mucho.

SCORE _____

Nombre _____ Clase _____ Fecha _____

Quiz 9-3A

CAPÍTULO 9

C. Beatriz and Laura are shopping at a vintage clothing store. Complete their conversation with the clerk with the missing expressions. Use each expression only once. (8 points)

> prefiero   Cuál de   la gris   cuesta   Además
> Te queda   Cuánto cuestan   me gusta más

BEATRIZ   Perdón, señorita. ¿**17.** _____ estas faldas?

CLERK   La negra es 15 dólares. La falda gris **18.** _____ 12 dólares.

BEATRIZ   Gracias. Laura, mira... ¿**19.** _____ estas faldas prefieres? ¿La

negra o **20.** _____?

LAURA   Este... pues, creo que **21.** _____ la negra.

BEATRIZ   A mí también **22.** _____.

CLERK   **23.** _____ muy bien. **24.** _____, el negro es

un color muy elegante.

SCORE [   ]

D. What Spanish expression would you use to say that something is . . .? (6 points)

25. a bargain _____

26. expensive _____

27. a rip-off _____

28. cheap _____

SCORE [   ]

TOTAL SCORE [   ] /35

232 Testing Program

Spanish 1 ¡Ven conmigo!, Chapter 9

Copyright © by Holt, Rinehart and Winston. All rights reserved.

Nombre _____ Clase _____ Fecha _____

¡Vamos de compras!

Quiz 9-3B

■ TERCER PASO

Maximum Score: 35

I. Listening

A. Guillermo is asking you some questions. Find the logical answer and write the letter of your choice. (10 points)

1. _____
   a. El azul es muy bonito.   **b.** Prefiero comprar las blancas.   **c.** Prefiero la roja porque te queda bien.

2. _____
   a. No me quedan bien.   **b.** Son caros, $56.00.   **c.** Los pardos son más baratos.

3. _____
   a. Es caro. ¡Qué robo!   **b.** Me queda muy bien.   **c.** El collar es más caro que los aretes.

4. _____
   a. No. Son blancas.   **b.** Sí, y son muy baratas.   **c.** Te quedan bien.

5. _____
   a. Prefiero el pardo.   **b.** Prefiero las rojas.   **c.** Prefiero los negros.

SCORE [   ]

II. Reading

B. Look at the pictures and sentences below. Write the letter of the picture that corresponds to each sentence. (10 points)

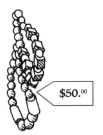
$50.⁰⁰

a.   b.   c.   d.   e.

_____ 6. Te quedan muy bien los cuadros.

_____ 7. ¡Qué ganga es este collar!

_____ 8. Las pardas allí son muy caras, ¿no?

_____ 9. ¿Te gustan las rayas?

_____ 10. Busco unos zapatos de cuero baratos.

SCORE [   ]

Quiz 9-3B

III. Writing

C. You're shopping at a department store in Caracas. Write a sentence in Spanish for each of the following situations. (9 points)

How would you . . .?

11. say you prefer this green dress to that blue one and tell why

_____

_____

12. ask how much those black sandals cost

_____

_____

13. say that you like these shorts because they fit you well

_____

_____

SCORE [   ]

IV. Culture

D. Based on the information in your book, respond with **a) cierto** or **b) falso** to the following statements. (6 points)

_____ 14. The monetary unit for Colombia, Spain, and Argentina is the **euro**.

_____ 15. Some currencies in Latin American countries are named for people.

SCORE [   ]

TOTAL SCORE [   ] /35

CUMULATIVE SCORE FOR QUIZZES 1–3 [   ] /100

9 ¡Vamos de compras!

Chapter 9 Test

I. Listening

Maximum Score: 30 points

A. Listen as several friends talk about the clothes they need. Based on what they need, decide what kind of event or place they must be going to: **a) un baile formal, b) la piscina, c) el colegio,** or **d) un viaje a Colorado en el invierno.** Write the letter of the place or event that is most appropriate for the clothing mentioned. (15 points)

1. _____   2. _____   3. _____   4. _____   5. _____   SCORE [____]

B. Rogelio is a Chilean student visiting Mexico. Listen as he and his friend Chantal discuss different gifts Rogelio would like to take home to his family. Then find the best answer to the statements that follow. (15 points)

_____ 6. Based on the illustrations, Rogelio _____ find all the stores he needs to buy the gifts he plans to buy.
   a. will   **b.** will not

_____ 7. Write the letter of the store where Rogelio will probably buy the present he is planning for his younger brother Julián.

_____ 8. The dresses at the department store are _____ the dresses at the Tienda Juárez.
   a. more expensive than   **c.** the same price as
   b. less expensive than

_____ 9. Chantal _____ think that Rogelio should buy his sister a more formal type of dress.
   a. does   **b.** doesn't

_____ 10. Right after this conversation, Rogelio will probably _____.
   a. go straight to the shoe store   **c.** go straight home
   b. invite Chantal to have a bite to eat

Juguetes   FLORERIA   ZAPATERIA   JOYERIA MENDEZ   DULCERIA-CONFITES

a.   b.   c.   d.   e.

SCORE [____]

Chapter 9 Test

II. Reading

Maximum Score: 27 points

C. Mariana left the message below for her friend. She wrote it in a hurry and didn't list her plans step by step. Show what she plans to do today by writing the letters of the sentences in the blanks in the correct order. (15 points)

11. _____

12. _____

13. _____

14. _____

15. _____

a. Después de comprarle esos regalos, quiero comprarles una planta nueva a mis padres.

b. A mi hermana le gusta mucho la ropa nueva.

c. Voy a regalarle un vestido elegante y unos aretes nuevos.

d. Voy a la florería para comprarla. Finalmente, regreso a casa para ayudar a mi mamá.

e. Necesito comprar unos regalos para mi familia.

SCORE _____

D. Read the conversation between Juan and Tomás as they go shopping for gifts. Then complete the sentences on page 237 by choosing the correct letter for each. (12 points)

TOMÁS   Hola, Juan. ¿Qué tal?

JUAN   Bien, gracias. ¿Adónde vas?

TOMÁS   Al centro. Tengo que ir de compras. ¿Quieres ir conmigo?

JUAN   Claro. ¿Qué vas a comprar?

TOMÁS   Mi prima Marta tiene su cumpleaños el jueves y quiero regalarle algo especial.

JUAN   ¿Qué piensas darle?

TOMÁS   Tengo muchas ideas, pero no sé todavía.

JUAN   ¿Qué le gusta hacer? ¿Le gusta nadar, leer o escuchar música?

TOMÁS   Los tres, pero le gusta más nadar. ¡Ya sé! Pienso comprarle un traje de baño. Vamos a buscarlo en el almacén del centro.

JUAN   Está bien. ¿Dónde está la tienda? ¿Cerca o lejos?

TOMÁS   Bastante cerca, al lado de la juguetería.

JUAN   Bueno, yo necesito algo para mi hermano. Prefiero regalarle un juego de mesa. No tengo mucho dinero, por eso necesito comprar un regalo bastante barato.

En la tienda

TOMÁS   Perdón, señorita. ¿Cuánto cuesta este traje de baño rojo?

EMPLEADA   ¿El rojo? El precio es $62.00.

TOMÁS   ¡Qué caro! ¿Y el morado?

EMPLEADA   Cuesta sólo $45.00.

TOMÁS   Cuesta demasiado. Pues, tengo que buscar algo diferente.

JUAN   ¿Por qué no buscas una blusa o un cinturón?

TOMÁS   Una blusa sí, pero a ella no le gustan los cinturones. Por allí hay unas blusas bonitas. ¡Vámonos!

JUAN   Aquí está una blusa de rayas que no cuesta mucho. ¿Te gusta? Es perfecta para el verano.

TOMÁS   Sí, pero prefiero esta blusa anaranjada porque es más barata. ¿Cuánto es esa blusa?

EMPLEADA   ¿Esa negra allí? No cuesta mucho. Es una ganga.

TOMÁS   Muy bien. Quiero comprarla.

16. Tomás is looking for clothing that can be worn _____.
    a. year-round
    b. in the winter
    c. in the summer

17. In choosing a gift, Juan takes into consideration _____.
    a. only price
    b. price and what the person likes to do
    c. only what the person likes to do

18. Tomás _____.
    a. doesn't like belts
    b. is on a limited budget
    c. likes both music and swimming

19. The gift Tomás would like to give his cousin is a _____.
    a. blouse
    b. swimsuit
    c. board game

SCORE ☐

Chapter 9 Test

III. Culture
Maximum Score: 13 points

E. Read the statements below. Based on the information in your textbook, determine whether the statements are **a) cierto** or **b) falso**. (9 points)

_____ 20. Spanish-speaking teens rarely wear bluejeans.

_____ 21. Much of what is stylish in the United States is also popular in Spain and Latin America.

_____ 22. Spanish-speaking shoppers may prefer to go to small specialty stores rather than large supermarkets.

SCORE [   ]

F. Discuss what kinds of clothes Spanish-speaking teenagers consider stylish. (4 points)

23. _____

_____

_____

_____

SCORE [   ]

IV. Writing
Maximum Score: 30 points

G. Look at the offers below. Using the prices shown, write a sentence in Spanish comparing the first item to the second. Say whether it is more expensive, less expensive, or the same price. (12 points)

$35 $25 $8 $10 $12 $12   seda $30   lana $20

24. los zapatos negros/los zapatos blancos

_____

_____

Spanish 1 ¡Ven conmigo!, Chapter 9

25. el cinturón corto/el cinturón largo

    _____

    _____

26. la camiseta blanca/la blusa negra

    _____

    _____

27. las corbatas de seda/las corbatas de lana

    _____

    _____

SCORE [＿＿＿]

H. Roberto and Tina are shopping for summer clothes. Write four sentences in Spanish based on the following situation. (8 points)

- Roberto says he likes this red shirt more than that blue one.
- Tina tells Roberto he looks good in the red shirt.
- Roberto asks Tina if she is going to buy anything for her cousins.
- Tina says she is going to buy them some T-shirts.

28. ROBERTO _____

    _____

29.   TINA _____

    _____

30. ROBERTO _____

    _____

31.   TINA _____

    _____

SCORE [＿＿＿]

Chapter 9 Test

I. Describe what clothes you like to wear when you go to a party, to school, and to the beach. Include colors and a complete outfit in your description. (10 points)

32. _____

_____

_____

_____

_____

_____

_____

_____

_____

_____

_____

SCORE [   ]

TOTAL SCORE [   ] /100

Nombre _____ Clase _____ Fecha _____

Circle the letter that matches the most appropriate response.

I. Listening
Maximum Score: 30 points

A. (15 points)

1. a b c d
2. a b c d
3. a b c d
4. a b c d
5. a b c d

SCORE [ ]

B. (15 points)

6. a b c d e
7. a b c d e
8. a b c d e
9. a b c d e
10. a b c d e

SCORE [ ]

II. Reading
Maximum Score: 27 points

C. (15 points)

11. a b c d e
12. a b c d e
13. a b c d e
14. a b c d e
15. a b c d e

SCORE [ ]

D. (12 points)

16. a b c
17. a b c
18. a b c
19. a b c

SCORE [ ]

III. Culture
Maximum Score: 13 points

E. (9 points)

20. a b
21. a b
22. a b

SCORE [ ]

F. (4 points)

23. _____
_____
_____
_____

SCORE [ ]

Nombre _____ Clase _____ Fecha _____

IV. Writing

Maximum Score: 30 points

G. (12 points)

24. _____

_____

25. _____

_____

26. _____

_____

27. _____

_____

SCORE [   ]

H. (8 points)

28. _____

29. _____

30. _____

31. _____

SCORE [   ]

I. (10 points)

32. _____

_____

_____

_____

_____

_____

SCORE [   ]

TOTAL SCORE [/100]

Spanish 1 ¡Ven conmigo!, Chapter 9

Listening Scripts for Quizzes 9-1B, 9-2B, 9-3B

CAPÍTULO 9

Quiz 9-1B Capítulo 9 Primer paso

I. Listening
A. Voy a comprar unos aretes para mi mamá y para mi hermana menor quiero comprar unos zapatos rojos de cuero. Le voy a regalar unas flores a mi abuela. A Paco le voy a dar unos juguetes nuevos. A mi papá le compro una corbata muy cara.

Quiz 9-2B Capítulo 9 Segundo paso

I. Listening
A. 1. TÚ ¿Quién es Manolo?
ROSA Es el muchacho que lleva una camisa azul, pantalones blancos, botas pardas, pero no lleva un cinturón.
2. TÚ ¿Quién es Anita?
ROSA Es la muchacha bonita. Lleva una blusa, una falda de rayas y sandalias.
3. TÚ ¿Quién es Gloria?
ROSA Lleva un traje de baño de cuadros, pero no lleva zapatos.
4. TÚ ¿Quién es Julio?
ROSA Es el muchacho que lleva pantalones cortos, una camiseta morada y zapatos de tenis.
5. TÚ ¿Quién es Jorge?
ROSA Es el hombre viejo. Lleva un traje oscuro, una corbata amarilla y una camisa blanca.

Quiz 9-3B Capítulo 9 Tercer paso

I. Listening
A. 1. ¿Cuál de estas camisetas prefieres?
2. ¿Cuánto cuestan estos pantalones?
3. ¿Es caro o barato ese collar?
4. ¿Son de cuero estas botas pardas?
5. ¿Te gustan los zapatos negros o los pardos?

CAPÍTULO 9

ANSWERS Quiz 9-1A

A. (10 points: 1 point per item)
1. joyería
2. tienda de comestibles
3. flores
4. corbata
5. dulcería
6. juguetes
7. aretes
8. tarjeta
9. zapatería
10. pastelería

B. (12 points: 1 point per item)
11. le
12. le
13. te
14. les
15. les
16. te
17. me
18. nos
19. me
20. nos
21. me
22. nos

C. (8 points: 1 point per item)
23. al lado del
24. a dos cuadras del
25. café
26. a dos cuadras de
27. lejos de
28. cerca del
29. parque
30. lejos de

ANSWERS Quiz 9-1B

I. Listening

A. (10 points: 2 points per item)
1. d
2. c
3. b
4. a
5. e

II. Reading

B. (6 points: 1 point per item)
6. e
7. b
8. g
9. a
10. f
11. c

III. Writing

C. (10 points: 2 points per item)
12. Mis padres piensan regalarle unos aretes a mi hermana.
13. Yo pienso regalarle una cartera a mi papá.
14. Mi abuelo piensa regalarles unas camisetas a mis hermanos.
15. Mi papá piensa regalarle un collar a mi mamá.
16. Mi hermano mayor piensa regalarle unos juguetes a mi hermano menor.

IV. Culture

D. (4 points: 2 points per item)
17. a   18. b

ANSWERS Quiz 9-2A

A. (10 points: 1 point per item)
1. unos bluejeans
2. una camiseta
3. una camisa
4. unos pantalones cortos
5. un traje de baño
6. unas sandalias
7. una blusa
8. una falda
9. unos zapatos
10. un suéter

B. (6 points: 1.5 points per item)
11. una chaqueta de cuadros
12. unos calcetines de rayas
13. un traje anaranjado
14. un cinturón morado

C. (9 points: 1.5 points per item)
Some answers may vary. Possible answers:
15. La corbata es de seda.
16. Los suéteres de esquí son de lana.
17. La cartera es de cuero.
18. Las camisetas para niños son de algodón.
19. Las botas son de cuero.
20. Los calcetines de tenis son de algodón.

D. (10 points: 2 points per item)
21. El almacén es más grande que el boutique.
22. La ropa en el almacén es más cara que la ropa en Jazz.
23. Las personas que trabajan en el almacén son más simpáticas que las personas en el boutique.
24. La ropa formal en el almacén es tan elegante como la ropa formal en el boutique.
25. El almacén está menos cerca que el boutique.

ANSWERS Quiz 9-2B

I. Listening

A. (10 points: 2 points per item)
1. d
2. b
3. e
4. a
5. c

II. Reading

B. (12 points: 2 points per item)
6. no
7. sí
8. sí
9. no
10. no
11. sí

III. Writing

C. (9 points: 3 points per item)
Answers will vary. Possible answers:
12. La corbata de rayas es más fea que la otra corbata.
13. El cinturón es más caro que los calcetines.
14. La camiseta es tan cara como la camisa formal.

IV. Culture

D. (4 points: 2 points per item)
15. b   16. a

Spanish 1 ¡Ven conmigo!, Chapter 9
Testing Program **245**

Answers to Quizzes 9-3A, 9-3B

CAPÍTULO 9

ANSWERS Quiz 9-3A

A. (15 points: 1.5 points per item)
1. esta
2. esos
3. este
4. esas
5. esa
6. Ese
7. estas
8. este
9. estas
10. esas

B. (6 points: 1 point per item)
11. cuestan
12. cuesta
13. cuesta
14. cuestan
15. cuestan
16. cuesta

C. (8 points: 1 point per item)
17. Cuánto cuestan
18. cuesta
19. Cuál de
20. la gris
21. prefiero
22. me gusta más
23. Te queda
24. Además

D. (6 points: 1.5 points per item)
25. ¡Qué ganga!
26. ¡Qué caro!
27. ¡Es un robo!
28. ¡Qué barato!

ANSWERS Quiz 9-3B

I. Listening
A. (10 points: 2 points per item)
1. c
2. b
3. a
4. b
5. c

II. Reading
B. (10 points: 2 points per item)
6. c
7. a
8. e
9. b
10. d

III. Writing
C. (9 points: 3 points per item)
Answers will vary. Possible answers:
11. Prefiero este vestido verde porque es más bonito que el azul.
12. ¿Cuánto cuestan esas sandalias negras?
13. Me gustan estos pantalones cortos porque me quedan bien.

IV. Culture
D. (6 points: 3 points per item)
14. b   15. a

Scripts for Chapter 9 Test

I. Listening

A. 1. Necesito comprar un traje de baño nuevo y unas sandalias.
   2. Yo busco un vestido de seda y unos zapatos bonitos para la cita con mi novio el sábado.
   3. Mi familia y yo necesitamos ropa nueva. Vamos a comprar unas chaquetas de lana y unas botas de cuero.
   4. ¡Qué bonita es esta falda de cuadros! Y la blusa de algodón también.
   5. Este traje es perfecto. También necesito una corbata de seda y una camisa amarilla.

B. CHANTAL   ¿Qué piensas regalarle a tu hermano?
   ROGELIO   Le voy a dar un par de botas mexicanas.
   CHANTAL   Perfecto. Pero también piensas comprar un vestido de algodón para tu hermana Paula, ¿no?
   ROGELIO   Sí, cierto, pero ¿no crees que ella va a preferir algo más formal?
   CHANTAL   No, hombre. Además, tienen vestidos típicos mexicanos en el almacén. Y queda cerca de aquí, al lado de la Joyería Méndez.
   ROGELIO   Bueno, pero ¿cuánto cuestan los vestidos allí? Son muy caros, ¿no?
   CHANTAL   No es cierto. Son del mismo precio que los vestidos que compraste ayer y son muy bonitos. Ahora, ¿qué buscas para tu hermanito Julián?
   ROGELIO   No sé. Le gustan los juegos de mesa, ¿sabes? Hay un juego mexicano que se llama Patolli.
   CHANTAL   Buena idea. Ahora a ver... ¿dónde queda la tienda de juguetes?
   ROGELIO   No sé. Pero primero vamos a la pastelería, ¿sí? Después de tanto pensar, ¡tengo hambre!

Answers to Chapter 9 Test

CAPÍTULO 9

I. Listening Maximum Score: 30 points

A. (15 points: 3 points per item)
1. b
2. a
3. d
4. c
5. a

B. (15 points: 3 points per item)
6. b
7. a
8. c
9. b
10. b

II. Reading Maximum Score: 27 points

C. (15 points: 3 points per item)
11. e
12. b
13. c
14. a
15. d

D. (12 points: 3 points per item)
16. c
17. b
18. b
19. a

III. Culture Maximum Score: 13 points

E. (9 points: 3 points per item)
20. b
21. a
22. a

F. (4 points)
Answers will vary. Possible answer:
23. Spanish-speaking teenagers usually wear the same kinds of clothes that teenagers in the United States do. They wear bluejeans, T-shirts, tennis shoes, etc.

IV. Writing Maximum Score: 30 points

G. (12 points: 3 points per item)
24. Los zapatos negros son más caros que los blancos.
25. El cinturón corto es más barato que el largo.
26. La camiseta blanca es tan cara como la blusa negra.
27. Las corbatas de seda son más caras que las de lana.

H. (8 points: 1 point per item)
28. Me gusta esta camisa roja más que la azul.
29. Te queda muy bien.
30. ¿Vas a comprarles algo a tus primos?
31. Voy a comprarles unas camisetas.

I. (10 points)
Answers will vary. Possible answer:
32. Para ir a la escuela me gusta llevar unos bluejeans y una camiseta azul. También me gusta llevar calcetines blancos y zapatos de tenis. Para ir a una fiesta me gusta llevar un traje con unos zapatos negros y una corbata de seda. Para ir a la playa prefiero llevar un traje de baño y unas sandalias.

248 Testing Program

Spanish 1 ¡Ven conmigo!, Chapter 9

Copyright © by Holt, Rinehart and Winston. All rights reserved.

10 Celebraciones

PRIMER PASO

Maximum Score: 35

Grammar and Vocabulary

A. Read the sentences and decide which U.S. holiday each one describes. Write the Spanish name for the holiday. You may use some holidays more than once. (12 points)

1. Es en el mes de junio. _____

2. Es en el otoño. _____

3. Es en el mes de febrero. _____

4. Casi siempre comen pavo *(turkey)* ese día. _____

5. Es en el mes de mayo. _____

6. Es en el invierno. _____

7. Muchas ciudades celebran este día festivo con fuegos artificiales *(fireworks)*.

   _____

8. Muchas personas celebran este día con regalos y un árbol *(tree)* decorado.

   _____

9. Lo celebran en la primavera con huevos pintados, dulces y ropa nueva. _____

10. Es en el mes de julio. _____

11. Celebramos estos dos días festivos en dos años diferentes. _____

SCORE _____

B. Read the statements, then write a sentence saying what each person or group is doing right now. Use the correct form of the present progressive and choose from the infinitives below. (14 points)

> hacer la tarea   buscar un regalo   organizar su cuarto
> poner la mesa   leer el libro de español   beber agua   comer sándwiches

12. El cuarto de Ricardo está sucio.

    Él _____.

13. Nuria y yo tenemos hambre.

    Nosotros _____.

Quiz 10-1A

14. Tengo un examen de español mañana.

Yo _____ .

15. La mamá de Alonso tiene un cumpleaños mañana.

Alonso _____ .

16. Samuel y Pati tienen mucha sed después de la clase de ejercicio.

Ellos _____ .

17. Vamos a cenar en cinco minutos.

Tú y papá _____ .

18. Siempre hay mucha tarea en nuestra clase de ciencias.

Nosotros _____ .

SCORE [   ]

C. Leticia and her brother Pedro are getting ready for their mom's birthday party. Complete their conversation with the missing expressions. (9 points)

Crees que	está decorando	qué te parece si
creo que no	Me parece bien	Estoy colgando

LETICIA   Pedro, ¿qué haces ahora? Necesito tu ayuda.

PEDRO   Un momento. 19. _____ las decoraciones.

LETICIA   ¿Por qué no 20. _____ la sala Anita?

PEDRO   Porque necesita ayudar a papá en la cocina. Oye, ¿21. _____

ponemos unas sillas afuera, en el patio?

LETICIA   22. _____ . ¿Y qué hacemos con el pastel y los refrescos?

¿23. _____ debemos ponerlos en el patio también?

PEDRO   No, 24. _____ . Prefiero poner la comida en la sala.

SCORE [   ]

TOTAL SCORE [/35]

CAPÍTULO 10 Celebraciones

■ PRIMER PASO

Maximum Score: 35

I. Listening

A. Listen as Marcos talks about what his family is doing to get ready for **el Día de la Independencia**. Match each of the following pictures with what Marcos says. (10 points)

a.　　　　b.　　　　c.　　　　d.　　　　e.

_____ 1.　_____ 2.　_____ 3.　_____ 4.　_____ 5.

SCORE _____

II. Reading

B. Complete Carlos and Catarina's conversation with words and phrases from the word box. Use each word or phrase only once. (10 points)

| Creo que sí　Creo que no　Crees que　Qué te parece　Me parece bien |

CATARINA ¿ 6. _____ si hacemos una fiesta en mi casa el sábado?

CARLOS 7. _____.

CATARINA ¿Crees que debemos mandar invitaciones?

CARLOS 8. _____. ¿Por qué no llamamos a todos?

CATARINA ¿Quieres colgar las decoraciones juntos?

CARLOS Buena idea. Puedo traer los globos.

CATARINA Perfecto. Y ¿es posible empezar a las dos?

CARLOS 9. _____. Tengo una cita a la una, pero puedo llegar a las dos.

¿ 10. _____ necesitamos más discos compactos?

CATARINA No. Tengo muchísimos.

CARLOS Bueno, hasta luego entonces.

SCORE _____

Quiz 10-1B

III. Writing

C. Write complete sentences using the present progressive to tell what the people below are doing right now. Use the subjects listed to begin each sentence. (10 points)

11. Los alumnos

_____

_____

12. Nosotros

_____

_____

13. Los jóvenes

_____

_____

14. Tú

_____

_____

15. Mi hermana y yo

_____

_____

SCORE ☐

IV. Culture

D. Based on the information in your book, answer **a) cierto** or **b) falso** to the following statements. (5 points)

_____ 16. July 25 is a national holiday in Spain that celebrates the feast of Santiago.

_____ 17. Spanish-speaking girls celebrate their **fiesta de quinceañera** at 21.

SCORE ☐

TOTAL SCORE ☐ /35

10 Celebraciones

CAPÍTULO

■ SEGUNDO PASO

Maximum Score: 35

Grammar and Vocabulary

A. Complete the requests and responses people make before a surprise party with the correct missing expression. (7 points)

un momentito	me haces el favor de	me ayudas a
cómo no	Lo siento	traes	Perdóname

—Silvia, ¿**1.** _____ preparar los sándwiches esta tarde?

—**2.** _____ , pero no puedo. Esta tarde tengo clase de baile.

—Nelson, me **3.** _____ esas sillas, ¿por favor?

—Sí, **4.** _____ . ¿Las pongo en la sala?

—Ramón, pasa la aspiradora, ¿quieres?

—**5.** _____ , pero en este momento estoy limpiando la cocina.

—Rafael, ¿**6.** _____ llamar a la pastelería?

—Sí, **7.** _____ . Primero necesito colgar las decoraciones.

SCORE ☐

B. You need some help getting ready for a party. Read the situations, then use the expressions below to ask a friend for help with each problem. (8 points)

mandar las invitaciones	inflar los globos	poner los regalos en el cuarto
pasar las decoraciones	poner las sillas en la sala	colgar los globos
ayudar a limpiar la casa		traer helado y galletas

8. You need more food for dessert. _____

9. You need help cleaning the house. _____

10. You can't reach the box of decorations. _____

11. You have a lot of invitations to address and send. _____

CAPÍTULO 10

Quiz 10-2A

12. After the party, all the gifts need to be put in the bedroom. _____

13. You need to blow up 50 balloons. _____

14. You want to hang balloons outside and all over the house. _____

15. There aren't enough chairs in the living room. _____

SCORE [   ]

C. Juliana is babysitting her younger brother and sister for a weekend while her parents are out of town. Complete the instructions her parents left for Juliana, Emma and Marcos with the correct informal command. Use the verbs in parentheses. (20 points)

Juliana:

16. _____ (Preparar) espaguetis y una ensalada para la cena el sábado.

17. _____ (Ayudar) a Emma con su tarea.

18. _____ (Lavar) la ropa de Emma y Marcos.

Emma:

19. _____ (Hacer) tu tarea de matemáticas.

20. _____ (Poner) la mesa el viernes y el sábado.

21. _____ (Ir) a visitar a tu abuela el domingo.

22. _____ (Limpiar) tu cuarto.

Marcos:

23. _____ (Cuidar) al gato el viernes y el sábado.

24. _____ (Sacar) la basura todos los días.

25. _____ (Cortar) el césped el sábado.

SCORE [   ]

TOTAL SCORE [   ] /35

Spanish 1 ¡Ven conmigo!, Chapter 10

CAPÍTULO 10

10 Celebraciones

CAPÍTULO

■ SEGUNDO PASO

Maximum Score: 35

I. Listening

A. You and Ana are discussing what still needs to be done for tomorrow's party. First, read the responses. Then listen to Ana and choose the correct response for each question. (12 points)

a. Sí, un momentito. ¿Está cerca o lejos?
b. ¡Cómo no! Voy a inflar los globos ahora mismo.
c. Perdóname, pero no puedo porque no tengo tiempo.
d. Con mucho gusto, pero creo que no está en casa ahora.
e. Sí. ¿Qué tal si los pongo sobre tu cama?
f. Claro que sí, pero a ti no te gusta la música española, ¿verdad?

1. _____ 2. _____ 3. _____ 4. _____ 5. _____ 6. _____

SCORE [   ]

II. Reading

B. Luz, Paco, and some friends are talking about getting ready for a party this weekend. Luz mentions things they need or need to do, and Paco tells others what to do. Match what Luz says to the orders that Paco gives. (7 points)

LUZ

_____ 7. Toda la casa está muy sucia.

_____ 8. Necesitamos refrescos para la fiesta.

_____ 9. No tenemos los postres para la fiesta.

_____ 10. Necesito ayuda con las decoraciones.

_____ 11. Tu cuarto es un desastre.

_____ 12. No mandamos las invitaciones.

_____ 13. No tenemos música.

PACO

a. Trae helado y pasteles.
b. Llama a nuestros amigos e invítalos.
c. Ve a tu casa y trae unos discos compactos.
d. Limpia la sala y los cuartos de baño.
e. Pon los libros en el escritorio y la ropa en el armario.
f. Ve a la tienda de comestibles y compra refrescos.
g. Infla los globos.

SCORE [   ]

Quiz 10-2B

III. Writing

C. Mercedes and Gilberto are decorating for a party. Using the cues in the word box, create a conversation between them in which one asks for help with two tasks and the other responds. (12 points)

hacer el favor	en este momento	cómo no	claro que sí
ayudar a	perdóname	lo siento	con mucho gusto	un momentito

14. MERCEDES _____

15. GILBERTO _____

16. MERCEDES _____

17. GILBERTO _____

18. MERCEDES _____

19. GILBERTO _____

SCORE [   ]

IV. Culture

D. Based on the information in your book, answer **a) cierto** or **b) falso** to the following statements. (4 points)

_____ 20. For most people in Latin American countries, the civil ceremony for marriage is just a formality.

_____ 21. Most couples in Latin America have only a religious ceremony when they marry.

SCORE [   ]

TOTAL SCORE [   ] /35

CAPÍTULO 10

Spanish 1 ¡Ven conmigo!, Chapter 10

CAPÍTULO 10 Celebraciones

Quiz 10-3A

TERCER PASO

Maximum Score: 30

Grammar and Vocabulary

A. Today is the 18th, the day of Pilar's party. Complete the statements by explaining when she did things to get ready. Use the Spanish expressions for *last night, yesterday, the day before yesterday, last week,* and *last Saturday.* Look at Pilar's calendar to decide which expression to use. (5 points)

lunes	martes	miércoles	jueves	viernes	sábado	domingo
6	7	8	9	10	11	12
hacer listas de invitados y comida	hacer listas de invitados y comida	hacer listas de invitados y comida	hacer listas de invitados y comida	hacer listas de invitados y comida	llamar a los invitados	
13	14	15	16	17	18	19
			limpiar la casa	comprar la comida ___ preparar la comida	¡FIESTA!	

1. _____ Pilar hizo las listas de los invitados y la comida.

2. _____ ella limpió la casa.

3. Llamó a los invitados _____ .

4. _____ compró la comida.

5. Ella preparó la comida _____ .

SCORE [   ]

B. Tony wrote a description of what his family did to celebrate Thanksgiving this past year. Complete his description with the correct preterite forms of the verbs in parentheses. (15 points)

Nosotros 6. _____ (celebrar) el Día de Acción de Gracias el 27 de noviembre.

Todos 7. _____ (ayudar) con las preparaciones. Mamá y la tía Linda

8. _____ (preparar) mucha comida. Y mi papá 9. _____ (hacer)

Quiz 10-3A

nuestro postre favorito, pastel de calabaza *(pumpkin)*. Mis hermanos Laura y Ángel

10. _____ (decorar) la casa. Miguelito, mi hermano menor, los

11. _____ (ayudar). Yo 12. _____ (invitar) a mis amigos

Roberto y Leti a cenar con nosotros. Ellos 13. _____ (llegar) a las cuatro de la

tarde. Nosotros 14. _____ (cenar) a las seis. Después, yo

15. _____ (llamar) a mis primos en San Antonio para desearles *(to wish them)*

un feliz Día de Acción de Gracias.

SCORE [   ]

C. Delia's mom is asking her daughter if she's done all the things she was supposed to do this afternoon. Write Delia's answers to her mom's questions, using the correct preterite form of the verbs and the correct direct object pronoun. (10 points)

16. Delia, ¿ya lavaste la ropa? (sí)

_____

17. ¿Y compraste el pan para la cena? (no)

_____

18. ¿Cortaste el césped? (sí)

_____

19. ¿Y ayudaste a tu papá con el carro? (sí)

_____

20. ¿Limpiaste tu cuarto? (no)

_____

SCORE [   ]

TOTAL SCORE [   ] /30

Quiz 10-3B

■ TERCER PASO

Maximum Score: 30

I. Listening

A. Héctor is asking you some questions. Find the logical answer and write the letter of your choice. (10 points)

_____ 1. **a.** Sí, Luz habló mucho.
        b. No, pero miré la televisión.

_____ 2. **a.** Bailo con su amiga Luisa.
        b. Estudió para el examen de español.

_____ 3. **a.** Sí, la lavé para ayudar a mi mamá.
        b. Sí, la lava mi hermano todos los días.

_____ 4. **a.** Sí, lo compraron en la librería.
        b. No, no lo compré.

_____ 5. **a.** Juan tocó la guitarra.
        b. María y Gloria, y después, descansaron.

SCORE _____

II. Reading

B. Read Marilú's letter to her best friend. Then answer the questions on page 260. (10 points)

Querida Sara,

    Quiero decirte lo que pasó en mi fiesta de quinceañera. Muchas personas vinieron (*came*)—mis abuelos que viven en San Marcos, tía Anita y tío Pablo y mis primos de San Antonio y todos mis amigos de la escuela. Mis padrinos también vinieron y me regalaron un collar fantástico. Decoramos la casa con muchos globos y otras decoraciones. Mi mamá preparó mucha comida y una amiga de ella la ayudó. Tocamos muchos discos compactos, especialmente de la música de Selena. José y yo bailamos toda la noche—¡lo pasamos muy bien!

    Pues, tengo que irme. ¿Cuándo vas a visitar a tus abuelos? Después, ¡ven a Dallas a visitarme!

              Tu mejor amiga para siempre,

                  Marilú

Quiz 10-3B

6. What type of party does Marilú describe? _____

7. What gift did she like especially, and who gave it to her? _____

8. How was the house decorated? _____

9. What did Marilú's mom do to help with the party? _____

10. Who did Marilú spend a lot of time with at the party, and what did they do? _____

_____

SCORE [ ]

III. Writing

C. Write five sentences saying what you, your family, and your friends did yesterday to prepare for a party. Use the pictures as cues. (10 points)

| yo | mi abuelo | mi amiga y yo | mis hermanos | tú |

11. _____

12. _____

13. _____

14. _____

15. _____

SCORE [ ]

TOTAL SCORE [/30]

CUMULATIVE SCORE FOR QUIZZES 1–3 [/100]

Spanish 1 ¡Ven conmigo!, Chapter 10

CAPÍTULO 10

CAPÍTULO 10 Celebraciones

Chapter 10 Test

I. Listening

Maximum Score: 30 points

A. You will hear people make statements about what people are doing now, did in the past, or will do in the future. Decide whether the action is **a) past**, **b) present**, or **c) future**. (20 points)

1. _____ 2. _____ 3. _____ 4. _____ 5. _____

6. _____ 7. _____ 8. _____ 9. _____ 10. _____

SCORE _____

B. Listen as people explain what their favorite holiday is. Decide which holiday they refer to and write the letter of the correct holiday. (10 points)

a. El Día de los Enamorados
b. Las Pascuas
c. El Día de la Madre
d. El Día de Acción de Gracias
e. La Navidad

11. _____ 12. _____ 13. _____ 14. _____ 15. _____

SCORE _____

II. Reading

Maximum Score: 30 points

C. Julio is asking his friend Gilberto some questions about a party they are putting together. Write the letter of the correct response by each question. (8 points)

_____ 16. ¿Me haces el favor de comprar helado?

_____ 17. ¿Qué te parece si decoramos la casa?

_____ 18. ¿Crees que hay bastante bebidas?

_____ 19. ¿Me ayudas a inflar los globos?

a. Claro que sí. Voy al supermercado ahorita.
b. Con mucho gusto. Y después podemos colgarlos.
c. Buena idea, pero todavía no tenemos decoraciones.
d. Creo que no. Necesitamos más refrescos.

SCORE _____

Chapter 10 Test

D. Arnoldo is helping prepare for his dad's birthday dinner. Complete each of his statements to his little sister by choosing the correct letter. (10 points)

_____ 20. _____ los regalos que tía María compró en la sala, por favor.
   a. Pone
   b. Pones
   c. Pon

_____ 21. ¿Me traes un cuchillo de la cocina? _____ necesitamos para la carne de res.
   a. La
   b. Lo
   c. Le

_____ 22. _____ a la sala y trae una silla para tía María.
   a. Va
   b. Ve
   c. Vas

_____ 23. Necesito una cuchara para este tazón. ¿Me _____ traes, por favor?
   a. lo
   b. él
   c. la

_____ 24. _____ al supermercado para más leche.
   a. Corre
   b. Corres
   c. Corro

SCORE _____

CAPÍTULO 10

E. You have taken over the job of Madame Cortinas, a local advice columnist, while she is on vacation. Read the following letter she received. Then write six sentences giving advice to Aparte Alejandra. Use expressions from the word box, or, if you prefer, you may use words not shown in the word box. (12 points)

Querida Madame Cortinas,

¿Qué te parece? Estos días estoy saliendo con un chico que quiero mucho. Estoy completamente enamorada de (in love with) él. Salimos todos los fines de semana. Nos gusta cenar y hablar juntos. A veces vamos al cine para ver una película. El problema es que durante la semana nunca me llama y siempre cuando lo llamo, dice que está ocupado y que no tiene tiempo para hablarme. Creo que no está mal si lo llamo—que debemos pasar el rato durante la semana. Pero se pone enojado (gets angry) si yo insisto en hablarle. No sé qué hacer. No quiero perderlo. ¿Me puedes ayudar?

Aparte Alejandra

CAPÍTULO 10

Me parece que...	llamarlo durante la semana	salir con otros chicos
Creo que...	darle más tiempo	hacer otras cosas
No debes...	ser más independiente	Debes...	explicarle cómo te sientes

---

25. _____

26. _____

27. _____

28. _____

29. _____

30. _____

SCORE _____

Chapter 10 Test

III. Culture

Maximum Score: 10 points

F. Read the statements below. Based on the information in your textbook, determine whether the statements are **a) cierto** or **b) falso**. (6 points)

_____ 31. **El día del santo** is a day for Hispanic girls to celebrate their coming of age.

_____ 32. Festivals in Spanish-speaking countries often celebrate religious or military events.

_____ 33. **La fiesta de quinceañera** is very important in the life of many Spanish-speaking girls and is usually celebrated with special parties.

SCORE [   ]

G. Clara and Simón are getting married today in a Latin American country. Yet the wedding won't take place until three days from now. Explain why this is so. (4 points)

34. _____

_____

_____

_____

SCORE [   ]

IV. Writing

Maximum Score: 30 points

H. You're taking care of your younger brother while your parents are out for the evening. He's not cooperating like he ought to. Write five sentences ordering him to do different things using informal commands. Use the cue for the first sentence. (10 points)

35. Do your homework! _____

36. _____

37. _____

38. _____

39. _____

SCORE [   ]

CAPÍTULO 10

I. Imagine you're at the party below and are trying to get your friend Ramón to come. Write five sentences telling him what's going on right now to convince him that he'll have a good time. (10 points)

40. _____

41. _____

42. _____

43. _____

44. _____

SCORE ☐

Chapter 10 Test

J. Write a letter to your pen pal telling him or her about your last holiday celebration. Be sure to include whom you visited, what presents you bought for your family and friends, how you spent the day, who prepared the food, if you sang songs, and any other things you can remember. (10 points)

45. _____

_____

_____

_____

_____

_____

_____

_____

_____

_____

_____

_____

SCORE _____

TOTAL SCORE _____ /100

Spanish 1 ¡Ven conmigo!, Chapter 10

Nombre _____ Clase _____ Fecha _____

CAPÍTULO 10 Chapter Test Score Sheet

Circle the letter that matches the most appropriate response.

I. Listening
Maximum Score: 30 points

A. (20 points)

1. a b c
2. a b c
3. a b c
4. a b c
5. a b c

6. a b c
7. a b c
8. a b c
9. a b c
10. a b c

SCORE [   ]

B. (10 points)

11. a b c d e
12. a b c d e
13. a b c d e
14. a b c d e
15. a b c d e

SCORE [   ]

II. Reading
Maximum Score: 30 points

C. (8 points)

16. a b c d
17. a b c d
18. a b c d
19. a b c d

SCORE [   ]

D. (10 points)

20. a b c
21. a b c
22. a b c
23. a b c
24. a b c

SCORE [   ]

E. (12 points)

25. _____
26. _____
27. _____
28. _____
29. _____
30. _____

SCORE [   ]

CAPÍTULO 10

III. Culture

F. (6 points)   **G.** (4 points)

31. a b   34. _____

32. a b   _____

33. a b   _____

_____

SCORE [   ]   SCORE [   ]

IV. Writing

H. (10 points)

35. _____

36. _____

37. _____

38. _____

39. _____

SCORE [   ]

I. (10 points)

40. _____

41. _____

42. _____

43. _____

44. _____

SCORE [   ]

J. (10 points)

45. _____

_____

_____

_____

_____

SCORE [   ]

TOTAL SCORE [   ] /100

CAPÍTULO 10

Quiz 10-1B Capítulo 10 Primer paso

I. Listening

A. 1. En mi casa todos están muy ocupados. Están preparándose para el Día de la Independencia. Mi abuela está cocinando mole. ¡Qué rico!
2. Mi mamá está limpiando el suelo de la cocina. Estoy seguro que va a pedir ayuda porque no le gusta limpiar.
3. Güita, mi hermana, está sacando la basura. ¡Qué bueno que ella lo tiene que hacer esta semana!
4. No sé por qué mi hermano mayor no ayuda. Parece que siempre tiene que hacer la tarea a la hora de limpiar la casa. Ahora está leyendo un libro en la sala.
5. Mi otro hermano, Luis, tiene que cuidar a mi hermanita porque mi mamá está ocupada en la cocina.

Quiz 10-2B Capítulo 10 Segundo paso

I. Listening

A. 1. ¿Me puedes ayudar a decorar la casa?
2. ¿Me haces el favor de mandar las invitaciones?
3. ¿Me traes unos discos compactos para la fiesta?
4. Oye, ¿me haces el favor de ir a la pastelería?
5. ¿Puedes llamar a Juan a invitarlo a la fiesta?
6. ¿Me ayudas a poner los regalos en mi cuarto?

Quiz 10-3B Capítulo 10 Tercer paso

I. Listening

A. 1. ¿Hablaste por teléfono anoche?
2. ¿Qué hizo Juan ayer?
3. ¿Lavaste la ropa anteayer?
4. ¿Compraste el pastel para la fiesta?
5. ¿Quiénes nadaron el Día de la Independencia?

ANSWERS Quiz 10-1A

A. (12 points: 1 point per item)
1. el Día del Padre
2. el Día de Acción de Gracias
3. el Día de los Enamorados
4. el Día de Acción de Gracias
5. el Día de las Madres
6. la Nochevieja/el Año Nuevo/la Nochebuena/la Navidad/el Día de los Enamorados
7. el Día de la Independencia/la Nochevieja
8. la Navidad
9. las Pascuas
10. el Día de la Independencia
11. la Nochevieja, el Año Nuevo

B. (14 points: 2 points per item)
12. Él está organizando su cuarto.
13. Nosotros estamos comiendo sándwiches.
14. Yo estoy leyendo el libro de español.
15. Alonso está buscando un regalo.
16. Ellos están bebiendo agua.
17. Tú y papá están poniendo la mesa.
18. Nosotros estamos haciendo la tarea.

C. (9 points: 1.5 points per item)
19. Estoy colgando
20. está decorando
21. qué te parece si
22. Me parece bien
23. Crees que
24. creo que no

ANSWERS Quiz 10-1B

I. Listening

A. (10 points: 2 points per item)
1. b
2. e
3. a
4. d
5. c

II. Reading

B. (10 points: 2 points per item)
6. Qué te parece
7. Me parece bien
8. Creo que no
9. Creo que sí
10. Crees que

III. Writing

C. (10 points: 2 points per item)
Answers may vary slightly. Possible answers:
11. Los alumnos están bailando.
12. Nosotros estamos tomando un refresco.
13. Los jóvenes están escuchando música.
14. Tú estás mirando/viendo una película.
15. Mi hermana y yo estamos caminando en el parque.

IV. Culture

D. (5 points: 2.5 points per item)
16. a   17. b

ANSWERS Quiz 10-2A

A. (7 points: 1 point per item)
1. me ayudas a/me haces el favor de
2. Perdóname/Lo siento
3. traes
4. cómo no
5. Lo siento/Perdóname
6. me haces el favor de/me ayudas a
7. un momentito

B. (8 points: 1 point per item)
Some answers may vary. Possible answers:
8. ¿Me traes helado y galletas del supermercado, por favor?
9. ¿Me ayudas a limpiar la casa?
10. ¿Me pasas las decoraciones, por favor?
11. ¿Me ayudas a mandar las invitaciones?
12. ¿Me haces el favor de poner los regalos en el cuarto?
13. ¿Me ayudas a inflar los globos?
14. ¿Me haces el favor de colgar los globos?
15. ¿Me ayudas a poner las sillas en la sala?

C. (20 points: 2 points per item)
16. Prepara
17. Ayuda
18. Lava
19. Haz
20. Pon
21. Ve
22. Limpia
23. Cuida
24. Saca
25. Corta

ANSWERS Quiz 10-2B

I. Listening

A. (12 points: 2 points per item)
1. b
2. c
3. f
4. a
5. d
6. e

II. Reading

B. (7 points: 1 point per item)
7. d
8. f
9. a
10. g
11. e
12. b
13. c

III. Writing

C. (12 points: 2 points per item)
Answers will vary. Possible answers:
14. ¿Me ayudas a decorar la sala, por favor?
15. Claro que sí. ¡Con mucho gusto!
16. ¿Me haces el favor de pasarme los globos?
17. Lo siento, pero en este momento no sé dónde están.
18. Están en la mesa en la cocina.
19 Muy bien. Un momentito, por favor.

IV. Culture

D. (4 points: 2 points per item)
20. a   21. b

CAPÍTULO 10

ANSWERS Quiz 10-3A

A. (5 points: 1 point per item)
1. La semana pasada
2. Anteayer
3. el sábado pasado
4. Ayer
5. anoche

B. (15 points: 1.5 points per item)
6. celebramos
7. ayudamos/ayudaron
8. prepararon
9. hizo
10. decoraron
11. ayudó
12. invité
13. llegaron
14. cenamos
15. llamé

C. (10 points: 2 points per item)
16. Sí, ya la lavé.
17. No, no lo compré.
18. Sí, lo corté.
19. Sí, lo ayudé.
20. No, no lo limpié.

ANSWERS Quiz 10-3B

I. Listening

A. (10 points: 2 points per item)
1. b
2. b
3. a
4. b
5. b

II. Reading

B. (10 points: 2 points per item)
6. She describes a **fiesta de quinceañera**.
7. She liked the necklace her godparents gave her.
8. The house was decorated with balloons and other decorations.
9. She and a friend made a lot of food.
10. Marilú spent a lot of time with José. They danced all night.

III. Writing

C. (10 points: 2 points per item)
11. Yo decoré el pastel.
12. Mi abuelo limpió la cocina.
13. Mi amiga y yo inflamos los globos.
14. Mis hermanos mandaron las invitaciones.
15. Tú pasaste la aspiradora.

Scripts *for* Chapter 10 Test

I. Listening

A.   1. Luis mandó las invitaciones para la fiesta.
     2. Mis abuelos van a visitarnos el dos de junio.
     3. Los jóvenes tocaron la guitarra en la fiesta.
     4. Patricia está cocinando arroz con pollo.
     5. Miré la televisión y escuché la música.
     6. Mi hermana está poniendo la mesa.
     7. Usted limpió la cocina anteayer.
     8. Voy a colgar las decoraciones el sábado.
     9. Todos mis amigos van a ir a la fiesta.
    10. ¿Estás preparando los tamales o haciendo el pastel?

B. 11. Este día es importante en la familia para mostrar que la madre es una persona especial. Todos nosotros hacemos de todo y le damos regalos a ella.
    12. Nosotros celebramos en la casa de mis abuelos. Vienen también los tíos y los primos. Tenemos una comida especial después de ir a misa a las doce. Recibimos muchos regalos especiales.
    13. Mi día favorito es un día especial para los novios. Les mando tarjetas a mis amigos y recibo dulces y flores de mi novio. Es el catorce de febrero.
    14. Este día es mi favorito porque tenemos vacaciones de la escuela. Vamos a la casa de mis abuelos y comemos una comida especial — pavo, papas, legumbres y postres deliciosos.
    15. Me importa esta celebración en la primavera porque es un día religioso. También a los niños les gusta buscar y encontrar huevos de colores que ponemos en el jardín.

Answers to Chapter 10 Test

I. Listening Maximum Score: 30 points

A. (20 points: 2 points per item)

1. a	6. b
2. c	7. a
3. a	8. c
4. b	9. c
5. a	10. b

B. (10 points: 2 points per item)

11. c
12. e
13. a
14. d
15. b

II. Reading Maximum Score: 30 points

C. (8 points: 2 points per item)
16. a
17. c
18. d
19. b

D. (10 points: 2 points per item)
20. c
21. b
22. b
23. c
24. a

E. (12 points: 2 points per item)
Answers will vary. Possible answers:
25. Creo que necesitas hacer otras cosas.
26. No debes llamarlo durante la semana.
27. Debes ser más independiente.
28. Debes explicarle cómo te sientes.
29. Debes darle más espacio.
30. Sal con otros chicos.

III. Culture Maximum Score: 10 points

F. (6 points: 2 points per item)
31. b
32. a
33. a

G. (4 points)
Answers will vary. Possible answer:
34. Very often in Spanish-speaking countries, both a civil and a religious wedding ceremony are held. In this case, it is possible for one to come before the other.

IV. Writing Maximum Score: 30 points

H. (10 points: 2 points per item)
Answers will vary. Possible answers:
35. ¡Haz tu tarea!
36. ¡Pon la mesa!
37. ¡Come las verduras!
38. ¡Ayúdame a lavar los platos!
39. ¡Limpia/Organiza tu cuarto!

I. (10 points: 2 points per item)
Answers will vary. Possible answers:
40. Todos lo están pasando bien.
41. Hortencia está hablando con César.
42. Adriana está cantando unas canciones.
43. Tony y Tyler están comiendo.
44. Martín y Kisha están bailando.

J. (10 points)
Answers will vary. Possible answer:
45. La Navidad del año pasado visitamos a mis abuelos. Para los regalos, compré un libro para mi abuela y una corbata para mi abuelo. Mi abuela preparó jamón, pavo, papas, sopa y verduras. Mi tía Luisa preparó el pastel. ¡Qué rico! Luego, cantamos unas canciones. Lo pasamos muy bien.

Spanish 1 ¡Ven conmigo!, Chapter 10

Nombre _____ Clase _____ Fecha _____

Para vivir bien

■ PRIMER PASO

Maximum Score: 30

Grammar and Vocabulary

A. Complete each statement about what people are doing and saying in the health club today with the correct reflexive pronoun. (10 points)

— No voy a ir a la clase de natación hoy. No **1.** _____ siento bien.

— Después de levantar pesas, Emilia **2.** _____ ducha y **3.** _____ maquilla en el baño del gimnasio.

— Pedrito, **4.** _____ duchas antes de nadar, ¿verdad?

— Marta, ¿por qué vas a correr ahora? ¿No **5.** _____ sientes cansada?

— David y Laura siempre **6.** _____ estiran antes y después de su clase de ejercicio.

— ¡La clase de yoga es fabulosa! Nosotros **7.** _____ sentimos muy bien después de esa clase.

— Antonio, ¿por qué **8.** _____ peinas antes de hacer ejercicio? ¿Por qué no

9. _____ lavas el pelo después?

— Hola, Olga y Luisa. ¿Cómo **10.** _____ sienten ustedes? ¿Listas para la clase?

SCORE [   ]

B. Read each situation, then complete the statements about how each person or group feels with the correct form of **sentirse**. Remember to use the correct reflexive pronoun. (12 points)

11. El sábado Daniel y Adán jugaron al basquetbol por cuatro horas.

Ellos _____ cansados.

12. Mi hermano y yo comemos bien y hacemos ejercicio todos los días.

Nosotros _____ muy bien.

13. ¡Uf! Estudié hasta las doce de la noche anoche.

Hoy _____ mal.

14. Tú no descansaste mucho este fin de semana, ¿verdad?

¿Todavía _____ cansado?

Spanish 1 ¡Ven conmigo!, Chapter 11

Testing Program **275**

Quiz 11-1A

15. Graciela lleva una vida muy sana.

Ella casi siempre _____ bien.

16. Roberto y Luisa, ¿por qué tomaron ustedes tantos refrescos y helados ayer?

Hoy ustedes _____ muy mal, ¿verdad?

SCORE [   ]

C. Write a sentence explaining what each person or group in the picture does for exercise. Use a different verb in each sentence. (8 points)

MODELO   Ricardo y Raimundo corren después de clases.

17. mis amigos y yo

20. Micaela

19. el señor Urrutia

18. la señora Soto

17. _____

18. _____

19. _____

20. _____

SCORE [   ]

TOTAL SCORE [/30]

Spanish 1 ¡Ven conmigo!, Chapter 11

CAPÍTULO 11

CAPÍTULO

11

Para vivir bien

■ PRIMER PASO

Maximum Score: 30

I. Listening

A. Listen as several people discuss their activities. Write the letter of the drawing that corresponds to the activity mentioned in each dialogue. One drawing will not be used. (10 points)

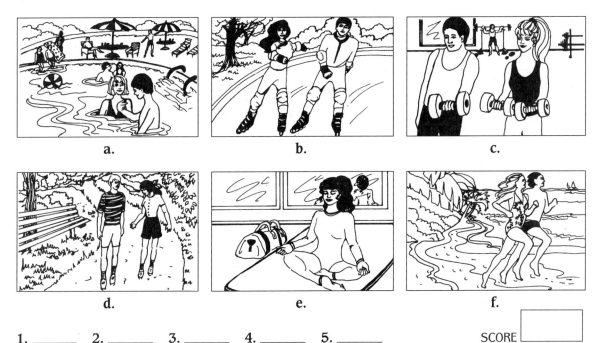

a.

b.

c.

d.

e.

f.

1. _____   2. _____   3. _____   4. _____   5. _____

SCORE [   ]

II. Reading

B. Luis is trying to get Manuel to exercise with him tomorrow. Read Luis's questions and choose the letter of Manuel's most appropriate response. (8 points)

_____ 6. ¿Por qué no patinamos sobre ruedas mañana?
    a. Gracias. Me gusta correr.
    b. No, en realidad no tengo ganas.
    c. No puedo porque me siento bien.

_____ 7. Pues, ¿qué tal si montamos a caballo mañana?
    a. No tengo ganas de hacerlo mañana.
    b. Te gusta montar a caballo.
    c. Te sientes mal, ¿verdad?

Quiz 11-1B

_____ 8. Pues, ¿quieres levantar pesas en el gimnasio mañana?
  a. Gracias, pero sólo me gusta patinar.
  b. Estoy un poco cansado. No quiero levantar pesas ahora.
  c. Gracias, pero no quiero.

_____ 9. ¿Qué tienes? ¿Te sientes mal?
  a. Sí. Tengo una cita con un médico (*doctor*) mañana.
  b. Sí, me siento bien.
  c. No me gustan los médicos.

SCORE [   ]

III. Writing

C. Write a conversation based on the following situation: Pablo and Ana meet. Pablo wants to go to the gym with Ana to do some exercise. Ana isn't feeling well. (12 points)

10. PABLO _____

11. ANA _____

12. PABLO _____

13. ANA _____

14. PABLO _____

15. ANA _____

SCORE [   ]

TOTAL SCORE [   ] /30

CAPÍTULO 11

Para vivir bien

Maximum Score: 35

■ SEGUNDO PASO

Grammar and Vocabulary

A. Read each statement, then summarize how each person feels using a logical expression with **tener** or **estar**. Use a different expression for each situation. (9 points)

1. Julián no puede respirar *(to breathe)* bien, y se siente cansado.

   _____

2. A Andrés le duele la garganta.

   _____

3. Ismael y Lucás no pueden jugar en el partido de voleibol hoy. Están enfermos y tienen que estar en casa.

   _____

4. Yolanda está en el baño, buscando el termómetro *(thermometer)* y unas aspirinas.

   _____

5. Samuel y yo nos sentimos muy mal. Tenemos frío y calor al mismo tiempo *(at the same time)*, y nos duele todo el cuerpo.

   _____

6. Esta tarde voy al médico para una inyección *(shot)*. ¡No me gustan nada las inyecciones!

   _____

SCORE [   ]

B. Little Benjamín is just learning the words for body parts. Help him by completing the explananation with the correct missing word. (12 points)

| piernas | cabeza | manos | oídos |
| ojos | brazos | dedos | boca |

Ben, el pelo está encima de la **7.** _____ . Y tienes dos **8.** _____

para ver las cosas. Los **9.** _____ son para escuchar, y la **10.** _____

es para hablar y comer. Y mira… necesitas las **11.** _____ para dibujar y pintar.

En cada una, hay diez **12.** _____ . Usas los **13.** _____ para levan-

tar cosas y las **14.** _____ para correr y montar en bici.

SCORE [   ]

Quiz 11-2A

C. While at the gym, people are talking about different aches and pains. Complete their conversations with the correct pronouns and forms of **doler**. (14 points)

— Tania, a ti **15.** _____ **16.** _____ la espalda después de levantar

pesas?

— No, pero a veces **17.** _____ **18.** _____ los brazos.

— Doña Ana, usted toma una clase de yoga, ¿verdad? ¿Todavía **19.** _____

20. _____ el cuello?

— No, ya no **21.** _____ **22.** _____ el cuello. Estoy muy bien, gracias.

— Ernesto y yo no vamos a correr hoy. A nosotros dos **23.** _____

24. _____ las piernas.

— A Lucinda y a Emilio **25.** _____ **26.** _____ las piernas también,

porque montaron en bicicleta por tres horas ayer.

— ¡La instructora de aeróbicos es increíble! Nunca está cansada, y parece que nunca

27. _____ **28.** _____ nada.

SCORE [   ]

TOTAL SCORE [   ] /35

Spanish 1 ¡Ven conmigo!, Chapter 11

CAPÍTULO 11

Para vivir bien

■ SEGUNDO PASO

I. Listening

A. Write the letter of the picture that indicates the body part that would most likely hurt in each of these situations. (8 points)

1. _____   5. _____

2. _____   6. _____

3. _____   7. _____

4. _____   8. _____

SCORE _____

II. Reading

B. Read Jaime's New Year's resolutions. Then answer the questions that follow. (12 points)

Hoy es la Nochevieja y éstas son mis resoluciones para el año nuevo. Por lo general, voy a llevar una vida más sana que la del año pasado. No quiero estar mal nunca. Quiero sentirme bien todo el tiempo y puedo hacerlo con estas resoluciones.

♦ Voy a comer por lo menos (at least) una comida balanceada al día. ♦ Voy a dormir por lo menos ocho horas cada día. ♦ Voy a hacer yoga todos los días. Es un ejercicio fantástico para el cuerpo. ♦ No voy a comer dulces ni tomar refrescos con mucha azúcar (sugar). ♦ Voy a ser un buen amigo. Voy a ayudar a mis amigos si están preocupados por algo. ♦ Voy a organizar mejor mi tiempo. No voy a estar nervioso ni enojado por no tener la tarea. ♦ Voy a tratar de ser optimista. No voy a estar triste a causa de (because of) cosas insignificantes.

9. What is Jaime's goal for the next year?

_____

_____

CAPÍTULO 11

Quiz 11-2B

10. How does he plan to achieve his goal?

_____

11. What is Jaime planning to do to improve his diet?

_____

12. How is Jaime intending to change his moods?

_____

SCORE _____

III. Writing

C. For each picture below, write a sentence saying how you think each person or couple feels and what they did that caused them to feel that way. (10 points)

| **Mario y Lastenia** | **Margarita** | **Diego** | **Yuka** | **Cristóbal** |

13. _____

14. _____

15. _____

16. _____

17. _____

SCORE _____

IV. Culture

D. Based on the information in your book, answer **a) cierto** or **b) falso** to the following statements. (5 points)

_____ 18. Roberto Clemente was a famous soccer player from Puerto Rico.

_____ 19. Many major league baseball teams in the United States have had Spanish-speaking players from Spanish-speaking countries.

SCORE _____

TOTAL SCORE _____ /35

Spanish 1 ¡Ven conmigo!, Chapter 11

CAPÍTULO 11

Nombre _____ Clase _____ Fecha _____

Para vivir bien

Quiz 11-3A

Maximum Score: 35

■ TERCER PASO

Grammar and Vocabulary

A. Andrés is talking about the fun he had last week. Complete what he says with the missing preterite forms of **jugar**. (9 points)

El lunes pasado Marcos y yo **1.** _____ al tenis en el parque. Más tarde, yo

2. _____ al baloncesto con unos amigos. El viernes por la noche mis hermanos y

yo **3.** _____ unos videojuegos nuevos. Mi papá **4.** _____ a las cartas

con mis abuelos, y mis hermanitos **5.** _____ un juego de mesa muy divertido.

¿Y tú? ¿**6.** _____ a un deporte la semana pasada?

SCORE ☐

B. Elisa plays soccer, tennis, and volleyball, and is telling her grandmother about the results of some recent games. Complete their conversation with the correct preterite forms of **ganar**. (12 points)

ABUELA   ¿Qué tal el partido de fútbol? ¿Quiénes **7.** _____ ?

ELISA   Les **8.** _____ nosotros. ¡Fue un partido fabuloso!

ABUELA   ¿Y el partido de tenis ayer? **9.** _____ tú, ¿verdad?

ELISA   No, no lo **10.** _____ . Lo **11.** _____ mi amiga Inés. Ella

juega muy bien.

ABUELA   Y cuéntame qué pasó en el partido de voleibol el jueves. ¿**12.** _____

ustedes?

ELISA   Pues, no **13.** _____ nosotros, ni **14.** _____ el otro equipo.

Fue un empate *(tie)*.

SCORE ☐

CAPÍTULO 11

Spanish 1 ¡Ven conmigo!, Chapter 11

Testing Program **283**

Nombre _____ Clase _____ Fecha _____

 Quiz 11-3A

C. Everyone in Herlinda's family did something athletic this week. Complete the sentences about where everyone went with the correct preterite form of **ir** in the first blank, and the most logical place for that sport or activity in the second blank. Mention each place only once. (14 points)

15. Efraín y yo _____ a las _____ para jugar al tenis el viernes.

16. Mi tío _____ al _____ para ver un partido de béisbol el domingo.

17. El sábado, mis hermanos _____ a las _____ para jugar fútbol con unos amigos.

18. ¿Cuándo _____ tú a la _____ para nadar? ¿Ayer o anteayer?

19. Rebeca _____ al _____ para levantar pesas anoche

20. Ayer por la tarde, yo _____ a la _____ para hacer atletismo *(track and field).*

21. Y mi abuela y sus dos perros _____ al _____ para caminar y ver a la gente.

SCORE [ ]

TOTAL SCORE [/35]

Spanish 1 ¡Ven conmigo!, Chapter 11

■ TERCER PASO

I. Listening

A. Olga and Ernesto are speaking to their friend Mario about what they did and where they went last Saturday. Listen to their conversation and then answer the questions below. (12 points)

_____ 1. Olga y Ernesto fueron a comprar _____.
     a. dulces   **b.** discos compactos

_____ 2. A Olga le gusta _____.
     a. escuchar música   **b.** bailar

_____ 3. Olga y Ernesto fueron _____.
     a. a la pastelería   **b.** a la juguetería

_____ 4. Ernesto fue a _____.
     a. la piscina   **b.** la biblioteca

_____ 5. Olga fue a casa y _____.
     a. lavó la ropa   **b.** caminó con el perro

_____ 6. Olga piensa que Ernesto es _____.
     a. flojo   **b.** inteligente

SCORE [   ]

II. Reading

B. Olivia and Ramón are talking about where people went and what sports they played yesterday. Read their conversation, then answer the questions that follow. (12 points)

RAMON   Olivia, ¿adónde fueron Mariana y Paloma ayer?
OLIVIA   A las canchas de tenis, para jugar unos partidos. Y creo que Paloma fue a la piscina después.
RAMON   ¿Nadaron también Rolando y Carlos?
OLIVIA   No, ellos fueron al estadio para ver el partido. ¿Y adónde fue Luis?
RAMON   A las cuatro él fue a la pista para el entrenamiento _(practice)_.
OLIVIA   ¿Fuiste tú con él?
RAMON   No, yo jugué al fútbol con José.
OLIVIA   ¿Fueron ustedes a la cancha al lado del colegio?
RAMON   No, al parque. ¿Y tú? ¿Por qué no jugaste al tenis o nadaste ayer?
OLIVIA   Porque decidí _(I decided)_ levantar pesas.

CAPÍTULO 11

Quiz 11-3B

7. Who watched a baseball game yesterday? _____

8. Which person participated in track and field? _____

9. Who played tennis yesterday? _____

10. Where did Ramón go to play soccer? _____

11. Who probably went to the gym? _____

12. Who did more than one sport yesterday? _____

SCORE [   ]

III. Writing

C. Look at the pictures below and tell where people went and what they did in each place. Use the cues to begin each sentence. (9 points)

13. Ellos _____

_____

14. Yo _____

_____

15. Tú _____

_____

SCORE [   ]

IV. Culture

D. Based on the information in your book, answer **a) cierto** or **b) falso** to the following statements. (2 points)

_____ 16. Football is as important in the U.S. as it is in Latin American countries.

_____ 17. Jai alai is a card game that originated in Mexico.

SCORE [   ]

TOTAL SCORE [   ] /35

CUMULATIVE SCORE FOR QUIZZES 1–3 [   ] /100

Spanish 1 ¡Ven conmigo!, Chapter 11

CAPÍTULO 11

Para vivir bien

I. Listening

Maximum Score: 30 points

A. Listen as people say what they do. Decide what symptoms they probably have and indicate what is wrong with each person. (10 points)

1. _____
2. _____
3. _____
4. _____
5. _____

   a. Le duele la mano.
   b. Tiene gripe.
   c. Está triste.
   d. Le duelen las piernas.
   e. Está nerviosa.

SCORE [ ]

B. You overhear two dialogues between people talking about illnesses. Respond to the following statements with **a) sí** or **b) no**. (20 points)

Diálogo 1

_____ **6.** A Luisa le duele la garganta.

_____ **7.** Rosa dice que Luisa debe ir a la clínica.

_____ **8.** A Luisa le gusta ir al médico.

_____ **9.** Luisa piensa que nunca va a estar mejor.

_____ **10.** Luisa decide llamar al médico.

Diálogo 2

_____ **11.** A Eduardo le duelen las piernas.

_____ **12.** Eduardo no puede jugar al fútbol por un año.

_____ **13.** Eduardo cree que caminó demasiado.

_____ **14.** A Eduardo le duelen los pies.

_____ **15.** Eduardo tiene fiebre y se siente mal.

SCORE [ ]

II. Reading

Maximum Score: 30 points

C. Read Dr. Pérez's description of his visit with his last patient, Enrique Ruiz. Then answer the questions that follow. (10 points)

> Hoy me visitó Enrique Ruiz. Pasé una hora examinándolo. Encontré los siguientes síntomas *(symptoms)*: tiene fiebre y tos. Tiene la nariz constipada y parece estar muy nervioso. Dice que trabajó 75 horas la semana pasada. Casi nunca descansa y muchas veces no desayuna ni cena. Es muy joven y también muy fuerte; tiene 28 años. Estoy un

Chapter 11 Test

poco preocupado porque no se cuida bien. La vez pasada que me visitó tenía *(he had)* los mismos síntomas. Hoy no le quiero dar medicina porque creo que es lo suficiente fuerte para recuperarse él mismo. Él tiene gripe—nada más. Tiene que descansar y tomar mucha agua y jugo. Y no debe trabajar tanto. Es muy malo para la salud.

_____ 16. How much time did Doctor Pérez spend examining Enrique?
a. 15 minutes   b. one hour   c. one week   d. 75 hours

_____ 17. Which of the following symptoms did Enrique not have?
a. a cough   b. a fever   c. a sore throat   d. nervousness

_____ 18. Which of the following could explain why Enrique is so sick?
a. He doesn't take care of himself.   c. He doesn't eat right.
b. He works too hard.   d. All of the above.

_____ 19. What does the doctor think Enrique has?
a. the flu   b. the measles   c. a sore throat   d. a cold

_____ 20. What kind of treatment is Doctor Pérez going to prescribe?
a. none at all   c. a hearty meal
b. antibiotics   d. rest, relaxation, and lots of water and juice

SCORE [   ]

D. Roberto is very lazy. His friend Rubén is trying to get him to do something. Match Rubén's questions with Roberto's responses. (8 points)

_____ 21. ¿Qué tal si levantamos pesas?

_____ 22. ¿Por qué no vamos al cine? Dan una película buenísima.

_____ 23. ¿Te gustaría ir al Café Nueva Edad?

_____ 24. Pues, ¿qué quieres hacer?

a. Gracias, pero en realidad no quiero. Tomé demasiado café esta mañana.
b. Gracias, pero no quiero ver esa película.
c. ¿Por qué no miramos la televisión? Prefiero descansar en casa.
d. No tengo ganas. Nunca hago ejercicio.

SCORE [   ]

CAPÍTULO 11

Chapter 11 Test

E. Your friends are always coming to you for advice. Read each problem, then choose the best advice for each one. (12 points)

_____ 25. Tengo muchos problemas con mis clases de ciencias y español este año. Cuando hay exámenes en esas clases, me duele el estómago y me siento muy nervioso. ¿Qué debo hacer?
  a. Creo que si te sientes nervioso, no debes asistir a clase cuando hay exámenes.
  b. ¿Por qué no estudias con tus compañeros de clase antes de los exámenes?

_____ 26. Esta semana me siento mal y estoy muy cansada. No tengo ganas de salir ni de practicar deportes. ¿Qué necesito hacer para sentirme mejor?
  a. Parece que estás un poco resfriada. ¿Por qué no descansas en casa unos días?
  b. Creo que es mejor comer menos postres y más fruta.

_____ 27. Quiero hacer ejercicio, porque no me siento bien. Pero no soy muy atlético, y no me gusta practicar deportes con otras personas. Prefiero estar solo.
  a. ¿Por qué no vamos a las canchas esta tarde?
  b. ¿Qué tal si corres en el parque muy temprano por las mañanas?

_____ 28. Estoy preocupada por mi amigo Martín. Creo que le pasa algo. Está triste, pero no sé por qué. Quiero ayudarlo. ¿Qué debo hacer?
  a. Me parece que necesitas hablar con él. ¿Por qué no lo llamas después de clase?
  b. No debes estar triste. Si estás preocupada, debes hacer algo divertido.

_____ 29. Creo que estoy un poco gordo, y no me gusta estar así. Estoy triste y quiero ser más delgado. ¿Qué te parece? ¿Qué necesito hacer?
  a. ¿Qué tal si comes ensaladas y fruta todos los días? Y debes hacer ejercicio también.
  b. Si estás triste, ¿por qué no invitas a unos amigos a tomar un helado contigo?

_____ 30. No sé qué me pasa, pero estoy mal. Durante el día, me duele la cabeza, y casi siempre estoy nerviosa o enojada. Por las noches no puedo dormir *(to sleep)*. ¿Qué debo hacer?
  a. Me parece que necesitas dormir ocho horas todas las noches.
  b. Creo que te sientes mal por la cafeína. No debes tomar mucho café ni refrescos con cafeína.

SCORE _____

CAPÍTULO 11

Chapter 11 Test

III. Culture
Maximum Score: 10 points

F. Read the statements below. Based on the information in your textbook, determine whether the statements are **a) cierto** or **b) falso**. (6 points)

_____ 31. Most Latin Americans don't drink very cold drinks.

_____ 32. Football is not as popular as soccer in Latin American countries.

_____ 33. Over 500 baseball players from Spanish-speaking countries
have played for the major leagues in the United States.

SCORE _____

G. What is a common attitude among Latin Americans toward cold drinks? (4 points)

34. _____

_____

_____

SCORE _____

IV. Writing
Maximum Score: 30 points

H. Pick one patient from Dra. Demora's waiting room. Write a conversation between that patient and Dra. Demora. The doctor should ask the patient how she or he feels. The patient should tell the doctor how he or she is feeling, mentioning at least two symptoms. The doctor should decide what the patient's problem is. (12 points)

Spanish 1 ¡Ven conmigo!, Chapter 11

CAPÍTULO 11

Nombre _____ Clase _____ Fecha _____

35. DOCTORA _____
_____

36. PACIENTE _____
_____

37. DOCTORA _____
_____

38. PACIENTE _____
_____

39. DOCTORA _____
_____

40. PACIENTE _____
_____

SCORE _____

I. Write a postcard to your pen pal asking what he or she would like to this summer while visiting you. Suggest two or three things that you might do together. Remember, your pen pal loves sports and outdoor activities. (10 points)

41. _____
_____
_____
_____
_____

SCORE _____

CAPÍTULO 11

Chapter 11 Test

J. Write a sentence in Spanish saying where the people in each picture went and what they did there. Also say when they went. Use the cues to begin your sentences. (8 points)

| Carla y María | Víctor y yo | Sandra | tú |

42. _____

_____

43. _____

_____

44. _____

_____

45. _____

_____

SCORE [   ]

TOTAL SCORE [   ] /100

Spanish 1 ¡Ven conmigo!, Chapter 11

Nombre _____ Clase _____ Fecha _____

CAPÍTULO 11 Chapter Test Score Sheet

Circle the letter that matches the most appropriate response.

I. Listening   Maximum Score: 30 points

A. (10 points)   **B.** (20 points)

1. a b c d e   6. a b   11. a b

2. a b c d e   7. a b   12. a b

3. a b c d e   8. a b   13. a b

4. a b c d e   9. a b   14. a b

5. a b c d e   10. a b   15. a b

SCORE [ ]   SCORE [ ]

II. Reading   Maximum Score: 30 points

C. (10 points)   **D.** (8 points)   **E.** (12 points)

16. a b c d   21. a b c d   25. a b

17. a b c d   22. a b c d   26. a b

18. a b c d   23. a b c d   27. a b

19. a b c d   24. a b c d   28. a b

20. a b c d   29. a b

                                               30. a b

SCORE [ ]   SCORE [ ]   SCORE [ ]

III. Culture   Maximum Score: 10 points

F. (6 points)   **G.** (4 points)

31. a b   34. _____

32. a b   _____

33. a b   _____

                  _____

SCORE [ ]   SCORE [ ]

CAPÍTULO 11

Spanish 1 ¡Ven conmigo!, Chapter 11   Testing Program **293**

IV. Writing

Maximum Score: 30 points

H. (12 points)

35. DOCTORA _____

_____

36. PACIENTE _____

_____

37. DOCTORA _____

_____

38. PACIENTE _____

_____

39. DOCTORA _____

_____

40. PACIENTE _____

_____

SCORE [   ]

I. (10 points)

41. _____

_____

_____

_____

_____

_____

SCORE [   ]

J. (8 points)

42. _____

_____

43. _____

_____

44. _____

_____

45. _____

_____

SCORE [   ]

TOTAL SCORE [   ] /100

Spanish 1 ¡Ven conmigo!, Chapter 11

CAPÍTULO 11

Scripts for Quizzes 11-1B, 11-2B, 11-3B

Quiz 11-1B Capítulo 11 Primer paso

I. Listening

A. 1. — ¿Qué tal si vamos al gimnasio?
— Está bien. Necesito levantar pesas esta tarde.
2. — ¿Qué tienes? ¿Te sientes mal?
— No, me siento muy bien. Voy a nadar. ¿Quieres ir?
3. — ¿Por qué no vamos al parque hoy?
— Buena idea. Me gusta mucho patinar sobre ruedas.
4. — ¿Qué tal si vamos a la playa?
— Gracias, pero prefiero caminar por un rato.
5. — ¿Quieres ir conmigo a la playa?
— ¡Claro! Me encanta correr por la playa.

Quiz 11-2B Capítulo 11 Segundo paso

I. Listening

A. 1. Cuando estudio demasiado me duelen _____.
2. Cuando practico el piano, me duelen _____.
3. Cuando tengo tos, me duele _____.
4. Cuando corro mucho, me duelen _____.
5. Cuando estoy resfriada, me duele _____.
6. Cuando levanto pesas demasiado, me duelen _____.
7. Cuando como muchos dulces, me duele _____.
8. Cuando voy a un concierto de rock, me duelen _____.

Quiz 11-3B Capítulo 11 Tercer paso

I. Listening

A. MARIO ¿Qué hicieron ustedes el sábado pasado?
OLGA Oye, Ernesto. Vamos a decirle a Mario qué hicimos el sábado pasado.
ERNESTO Está bien. Primero, fuimos a la tienda de música y compramos unos discos compactos.
OLGA Lo pasamos muy bien en esa tienda. A mí me encanta escuchar música nueva. Entonces, fuimos a la heladería a comer helado muy bueno y después, a la juguetería para comprar un regalo de cumpleaños.
ERNESTO Luego, yo fui a la biblioteca a estudiar porque tengo un examen. Y Olga fue a la piscina a nadar y hablarles a unas amigas.
MARIO ¿Y por la noche?
OLGA Ernesto no hizo nada importante. Jugó al fútbol, descansó y miró la televisión. Yo ayudé a mamá a cocinar, a lavar la ropa y a limpiar la casa. ¡Qué flojo es Ernesto!
ERNESTO Espera un momentito. Yo ayudé un poquito, saqué la basura y lavé los platos. Tú jugaste a las cartas antes de acostarte.
MARIO Pues, me parece que pasaron un día muy interesante.
OLGA Sí, es verdad. Adiós, Mario.
MARIO Hasta mañana.

Answers to Quizzes 11-1A, 11-1B

ANSWERS Quiz 11-1A

A. (10 points: 1 point per item)
1. me
2. se
3. se
4. te
5. te
6. se
7. nos
8. te
9. te
10. se

B. (12 points: 2 points per item)
11. se sienten
12. nos sentimos
13. me siento
14. te sientes
15. se siente
16. se sienten

C. (8 points: 2 points per item)
Answers will vary. Possible answers:
17. Mis amigos y yo patinamos sobre ruedas en el parque.
18. La señora Soto hace yoga por las mañanas.
19. El señor Urrutia se estira en el gimnasio.
20. Micaela levanta pesas los fines de semana.

ANSWERS Quiz 11-1B

I. Listening
A. (10 points: 2 points per item)
1. c
2. a
3. b
4. d
5. f

II. Reading
B. (8 points: 2 points per item)
6. b
7. a
8. c
9. a

III. Writing
C. (12 points: 2 points per item)
Answers will vary. Possible answer:
10. PABLO Hola, Ana. ¿Cómo estás? ¿Qué tal si vamos al gimnasio hoy?
11. ANA Gracias, pero no puedo. No me siento bien.
12. PABLO ¿Qué te pasa? ¿Qué tienes?
13. ANA Me duele la cabeza y me siento muy cansada.
14. PABLO Ay, lo siento mucho. Tal vez, otro día, entonces.
15. ANA Sí. Voy a descansar un poco.

Answers to Quizzes 11-2A, 11-2B

ANSWERS Quiz 11-2A

A. (9 points: 1.5 points per item)
Answers will vary. Possible answers:
1. Está resfriado.
2. Tiene tos.
3. Están enojados/tristes. Tienen fiebre.
4. Tiene fiebre.
5. Tenemos gripe.
6. Estoy nervioso/a. Estoy preocupado/a.

B. (12 points: 1.5 points per item)
7. cabeza
8. ojos
9. oídos
10. boca
11. manos
12. dedos
13. brazos
14. piernas

C. (14 points: 1 point per item)
15. te
16. duele
17. me
18. duelen
19. le
20. duele
21. me
22. duele
23. nos
24. duelen
25. les
26. duelen
27. le
28. duele

ANSWERS Quiz 11-2B

I. Listening

A. (8 points: 1 point per item)
1. e   5. c
2. h   6. d
3. a   7. b
4. f   8. g

II. Reading

B. (12 points: 3 points per item)
Answers will vary. Possible answers:
9. He plans to lead a healthier life than he did last year.
10. He's going to exercise more, sleep more, and try not to have so much sugar.
11. Jamie's going to try to eat at least one balanced meal a day.
12. He's not going to be nervous, angry or sad.

III. Writing

C. (10 points: 2 points per item)
Answers will vary. Possible answers:
13. A Mario y a Lastenia les duelen los pies porque trabajaron toda la noche.
14. Margarita no se siente bien porque tomó muchos refrescos.
15. A Diego le duelen los oídos porque escuchó música por dos horas.
16. A Yuka le duelen las manos/los dedos porque tocó el piano por tres horas.
17. A Cristóbal le duele la pierna porque jugó al fútbol.

IV. Culture

D. (5 points: 2.5 points per item)
18. b   19. a

Answers to Quizzes 11-3A, 11-3B

ANSWERS Quiz 11-3A

A. (9 points: 1.5 points per item)
1. jugamos
2. jugué
3. jugamos
4. jugó
5. jugaron
6. Jugaste

B. (12 points: 1.5 points per item)
7. ganaron
8. ganamos
9. Ganaste
10. gané
11. ganó
12. Ganaron
13. ganamos
14. ganó

C. (14 points: 1 point per item)
15. fuimos, canchas de tenis
16. fue, estadio
17. fueron, canchas de fútbol
18. fuiste, piscina
19. fue, gimnasio
20. fui, pista de correr
21. fueron, parque

ANSWERS Quiz 11-3B

I. Listening

A. (12 points: 2 points per item)
1. b
2. a
3. b
4. b
5. a
6. a

II. Reading

B. (12 points: 2 points per item)
7. Rolando and Carlos
8. Luis
9. Mariana and Paloma
10. to the park
11. Olivia
12. Paloma

III. Writing

C. (9 points: 3 points per item)
13. fueron al cine a ver una película.
14. fui al estadio a jugar al béisbol.
15. fuiste a la tienda de discos a comprar unos discos compactos.

IV. Culture

D. (2 points: 1 point per item)
16. b   17. b

CAPITULO 11

Spanish 1 ¡Ven conmigo!, Chapter 11

Scripts *for* Chapter 11 Test

I. Listening

A. 1. Estamos en el restaurante y no tengo dinero para pagar la cuenta.
    2. No puedo correr más. Estoy cansado.
    3. Le escribo muchas cartas a mi abuela.
    4. Tengo tos y me siento mal.
    5. Mi novia va a vivir en otra ciudad.

B. Diálogo 1

ROSA   ¿Qué tienes, Luisa? Me parece que estás pálida.
LUISA   Estoy un poco resfriada y me duele la garganta, Rosa.
ROSA   ¿Por cuánto tiempo?
LUISA   Dos o tres días.
ROSA   Creo que debes ir a la clínica.
LUISA   No, porque no me gusta ir al médico. Mañana voy a estar mejor.
ROSA   Pues, estamos hablando de tu salud, Luisa. Debes ir a la clínica.
LUISA   Bueno, Rosa, voy a llamar al médico ahora mismo.

Diálogo 2

TOMÁS   ¿Qué te pasa, Eduardo? ¿Te sientes mal?
EDUARDO   Sí, me duelen las piernas y no puedo jugar al fútbol por una semana.
TOMÁS   ¿Qué te pasó?
EDUARDO   No sé, Tomás, pero el médico me dice que no debo asistir a la escuela ni caminar mucho.
          Creo que caminé demasiado anteayer.
TOMÁS   Lo siento. ¿Te duelen también los pies?
EDUARDO   No, pero tengo fiebre y me siento bastante mal.
TOMÁS   Pues, debes llamar al médico otra vez.

Answers to Chapter 11 Test

I. Listening Maximum Score: 30 points

A. (10 points: 2 points per item)
1. e
2. d
3. a
4. b
5. c

B. (20 points: 2 points per item)
6. a
7. a
8. b
9. b
10. a
11. a
12. b
13. a
14. b
15. a

II. Reading Maximum Score: 30 points

C. (10 points: 2 points per item)
16. b
17. c
18. d
19. a
20. d

D. (8 points: 2 points per item)
21. d
22. b
23. a
24. c

E. (12 points: 2 points per item)
25. b
26. a
27. b
28. a
29. a
30. b

III. Culture Maximum Score: 9 points

F. (6 points: 2 points per item)
31. a
32. a
33. a

G. (4 points)
34. Many Latin Americans avoid them because they believe that ice-cold drinks are harmful to the body, especially when suffering from a cold.

IV. Writing Maximum Score: 30 points

H. (12 points: 2 points per item)
Dialogues will vary. Possible dialogue:
35. DOCTORA   Buenos días. ¿Cómo te sientes hoy?
36. PACIENTE   Buenos días, doctora. Me siento muy mal. Me duele mucho la cabeza.
37. DOCTORA   ¿Tienes fiebre también?
38. PACIENTE   Sí, tengo una temperatura de 100. ¿Qué me pasa?
39. DOCTORA   Bueno, creo que tienes gripe. Debes descansar en casa y tomar mucho jugo de fruta.
40. PACIENTE   Gracias, doctora. Ahora voy a casa para tomar un jugo de naranja.

I. (10 points)
Answers will vary. Possible answers:
41. Hola, amigo/a,
¿Cómo estás? Yo, muy bien. Tengo muchas ganas de verte. ¿Qué te gustaría hacer este verano? ¿nadar? ¿patinar sobre ruedas? ¿montar a caballo? Durante el verano aquí hace mucho calor, por eso debemos nadar e ir a la playa con frecuencia. ¿Qué tienes ganas de hacer tú? Escríbeme pronto.

J. (8 points: 2 points per item)
Answers will vary. Possible answers:
42. El sábado pasado, Carla y María fueron al cine para ver una película.
43. Ayer Víctor y yo fuimos a las canchas de tenis y jugamos al tenis por una hora.
44. Sandra fue a la biblioteca el lunes para estudiar para un examen.
45. Anoche fuiste al gimnasio a levantar pesas.

Nombre _____ Clase _____ Fecha _____

12 Las vacaciones ideales

Quiz 12-1A

PRIMER PASO

Maximum Score: 30

Grammar and Vocabulary

A. Nélida is describing her daily routine at school and home. Complete what she says with the correct present-tense form of the missing verbs. Some verbs may be used more than once. (15 points)

empezar	tener	almorzar
poder	preferir	venir

Las clases en mi colegio **1.** _____ a las ocho y cuarto. Siempre salgo para el colegio a

las siete y media porque **2.** _____ desayunar en la cafetería allí y pasar el rato con

mis amigos. Mi hermano Iván es muy desorganizado y nunca **3.** _____ tiempo para

desayunar. Él y sus amigos **4.** _____ muchísima hambre toda la mañana. Yo

5. _____ a las once y media con mis amigas. Típicamente nosotras

6. _____ en la cafetería. Pero si hace buen tiempo, **7.** _____ comer en el

patio del colegio. Después de clases, a veces mis amigas **8.** _____ a casa conmigo

para mirar la televisión y pasar el rato. Esta tarde ellas no **9.** _____ venir, porque

todas nosotras **10.** _____ que estudiar mucho para el examen de ciencias mañana.

SCORE _____

B. This winter Teo is going on a ski vacation, while his friend Lauren is going to the Caribbean. Look at the lists of what they still have to get before leaving, then explain in Spanish what each person needs. Include the correct indefinite article. (10 points)

Teodoro
11. scarf
12. skis
13. camera
14. jacket
15. ticket

Lauren
16. sunglasses
17. suitcase
18. sandals
19. bathing suit
20. towel

Quiz 12-1A

11. _____

12. _____

13. _____

14. _____

15. _____

16. _____

17. _____

18. _____

19. _____

20. _____

SCORE [   ]

C. Lalo and Miguel are talking about plans for after school. Complete their conversation with the Spanish equivalents for the English expressions. Remember that some Spanish verbs require **a** or **que** before the infinitive. (5 points)

LALO   ¿Qué 21. _____ hacer hoy después de clases?
            (are we going)

MIGUEL   Hace mucho calor, ¿no? Yo 22. _____ ir a nadar. ¿Qué te parece?
                    (I want)

LALO   ¡Perfecto! Pero sólo puedo nadar una hora. A las cuatro y media

            23. _____ estar en casa.
                    (I have to)

MIGUEL   ¿Qué 24. _____ hacer en casa?
                    (do you need)

LALO   Pues, debo organizar mi cuarto. Oye, ¿25. _____ invitar a Rafa a
                                                            (are you going)

            ir con nosotros?

MIGUEL   Sí, buena idea.

SCORE [   ]

TOTAL SCORE [   ] /30

12 Las vacaciones ideales

Quiz 12-1B

■ PRIMER PASO

Maximum Score: 30

I. Listening

A. Listen as various people talk about places they plan to go and things they plan to do. Then decide where each person should go, and write the letter of your choice on your quiz sheet. (12 points)

- **a.** A la joyería
- **b.** A Puerto Rico
- **c.** Al colegio
- **d.** A la clínica
- **e.** A Nueva York
- **f.** A la dulcería

1. _____ 2. _____ 3. _____ 4. _____ 5. _____ 6. _____   SCORE [   ]

II. Reading

B. Read the descriptions three people have written about what they do during a typical day. Then read the quotes that follow and decide who would most likely have said each one: Carlota (**C**), Benjamín (**B**), or Salvador (**S**). (10 points)

Carlota
Me gusta mucho la escuela. Son muy interesantes todas mis clases. Durante el almuerzo me gusta estudiar y leer. Después de la escuela voy a la biblioteca a leer por una hora. Cuando regreso a casa, ayudo a mi mamá a preparar la cena. Muchas veces mis amigos quieren salir, pero yo no salgo porque prefiero estudiar. Es necesario estudiar mucho si quiero sacar buenas notas.

Benjamín
No me gusta mucho la escuela. Las clases que tengo son muy difíciles. Prefiero jugar al fútbol norteamericano con mis amigos. Siempre vamos al estadio a jugar los sábados. Después vamos a un café a tomar un refresco o algo así. Mi amiga Carlota muchas veces me invita a estudiar con ella en su casa pero prefiero pasar el rato con mis amigos.

Salvador
La escuela es muy interesante. Lo que me gusta más son mis clases de música. Toco el trombón en la banda y canto en el coro. Algún día espero ser compositor de música. Después de clases siempre practico tres horas.

_____ **7.** Para mí, lo más importante es la música.

_____ **8.** Algún día espero asistir al *Super Bowl*, el partido de fútbol norteamericano más famoso de los Estados Unidos.

Quiz 12-1B

_____ 9. Gracias, pero no puedo ir con ustedes hoy. Tengo que estudiar.

_____ 10. Hago ejercicio todos los días. Tengo que estar en buena forma para el partido este fin de semana.

_____ 11. Ahora mismo voy a practicar el piano. Tengo que tocar en el concierto mañana.

SCORE [   ]

III. Writing

C. For each of the following pictures, write a sentence saying what the person has in mind for the future. Use at least four different verbs from the word box. (8 points)

querer   pensar   ir a   poder   esperar

| Yuka | Pablo | Leonardo | María |

12. _____

_____

13. _____

_____

14. _____

_____

15. _____

_____

SCORE [   ]

TOTAL SCORE [   ] /30

12 Las vacaciones ideales

Quiz 12-2A

■ SEGUNDO PASO

Maximum Score: 35

Grammar and Vocabulary

A. Explain what each person or group is doing while on vacation. Use the correct form of the present progressive and a different verb for each sentence. (9 points)

Pilar

Luis y Curro

1. _____

2. _____

_____

_____

mi familia y yo

tú y Maricarmen

3. _____

4. _____

_____

_____

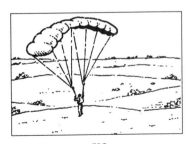

mis primos

yo

5. _____

6. _____

_____

_____

SCORE [   ]

Quiz 12-2A

B. Celia and a friend are talking about what Celia and her family would like to do on a dream vacation. Complete their conversation with the correct pronouns and forms of **gustar**. (10 points)

— Celia, ¿a ti qué 7. _____ 8. _____ hacer para las vacaciones este año?

— A mí 9. _____ 10. _____ ir a América Latina. ¡A mis hermanos y a mí

    11. _____ 12. _____ escalar montañas en los Andes y explorar en la selva!

— ¿Y a tus padres 13. _____ 14. _____ hacer esas cosas también?

— No, para nada. A mi madre 15. _____ 16. _____ hacer un

    viaje a Europa y visitar todos los museos de arte. ¡Qué aburrido!

SCORE [   ]

C. A science magazine is interviewing Mariana Trotamundos, a famous explorer and nature photographer. Complete the interview with the correct form of **ser** or **estar**. (16 points)

REVISTA   Buenos días y gracias por la entrevista. Mariana, dime... ¿de dónde

           17. _____ ?

MARIANA   18. _____ de Venezuela, y todavía tengo una casa en Caracas. Pero no

           19. _____ allí casi nunca, porque 20. _____ muy ocupada

    con mis viajes y mis videos.

REVISTA   ¿Y qué 21. _____ haciendo en estos días?

MARIANA   Un grupo de científicos *(scientists)* y yo 22. _____ haciendo una

    película sobre el Río Amazonas.

REVISTA   Mariana, viajas mucho y has visto *(you've seen)* muchos lugares. ¿Cuál

           23. _____ tu lugar favorito?

MARIANA   Los Andes, porque 24. _____ tan altos y misteriosos.

REVISTA   Pues, Mariana, gracias otra vez, y buena suerte con la película.

SCORE [   ]

TOTAL SCORE [/35]

12 Las vacaciones ideales

Quiz 12-2B

■ SEGUNDO PASO

Maximum Score: 35

I. Listening

A. Listen as Julia and Raúl talk about what various friends and family members like to do. Match each person to what he or she likes to do. (10 points)

a.   b.   c.   d.   e.

1. _____ 2. _____ 3. _____ 4. _____ 5. _____

SCORE [   ]

II. Reading

B. Read this advertisement for a summer camp, then decide whether the statements that follow are **a) cierto** or **b) falso**. (10 points)

> **¡Bienvenidos al Campamento Colinas Verdes!**
>
> **Gran variedad de actividades deportivas y recreativas**
> - acampar
> - saltar en paracaídas
> - ir de vela
> - bucear
> - pescar
>
> **Excursiones todos los días**
> - caminar por el bosque
> - bajar en canoa por el río
> - escalar montañas
>
> **Clases todas las semanas con instructores expertos**
> - buceo
> - esquí acuático
> - natación
> - tenis

_____ 6. This camp would not be good for someone who wants to scuba dive and sail.

_____ 7. If you're interested in parachuting, this would be a good camp for you.

_____ 8. This camp only offers water sports.

_____ 9. There are canoe classes taught every day.

_____ 10. You would have the opportunity to go on a mountain-climbing trip at this camp.

SCORE [   ]

Quiz 12-2B

III. Writing

C. Imagine you are on vacation in a wonderful place. Write a note to your friend about it, following the guidelines given. Write a complete sentence for each item. (10 points)

11. Tell your friend where you are.

_____

12. Explain how you are feeling.

_____

13. Describe the place.

_____

14. Say what you're doing right now.

_____

15. Explain what you and your family would like to do later today.

_____

SCORE [____]

IV. Culture

D. Based on the information in your textbook, answer **a) cierto** or **b) falso** to the following statements. (5 points)

_____ 16. **Paradores** are large, modern hotels found in all Spanish-speaking countries.

_____ 17. One **parador** in Spain is a castle built in the eighth century.

SCORE [____]

TOTAL SCORE [____] /35

Spanish 1 ¡Ven conmigo!, Chapter 12

Las vacaciones ideales

Quiz 12-3A

TERCER PASO

Maximum Score: 35

Grammar and Vocabulary

A. Ricardo and his friends stayed at home over summer vacation. Complete his conversation about what people did with the correct preterite forms of the verbs in parentheses. (15 points)

PILAR   Hola, Ricardo. ¿Qué tal las vacaciones? ¿**1.** _____ (Viajar) a algún

lugar?

RICARDO   No, pero yo lo **2.** _____ (pasar) muy bien aquí. **3.** _____

(Trabajar) en un restaurante mexicano los fines de semana y **4.** _____

(jugar) al baloncesto en el parque todos los días.

PILAR   ¿Y tu amigo Gonzalo? ¿Él **5.** _____ (jugar) contigo?

RICARDO   No, él **6.** _____ (tomar) unas clases este verano y **7.** _____

(estudiar) para sus exámenes. Pero nosotros **8.** _____ (hablar) por

teléfono todos los días.

PILAR   ¿Qué más hicieron ustedes? ¿**9.** _____ (Nadar) en el lago mucho?

RICARDO   No mucho, pero sí nadamos y **10.** _____ (pescar) allí tres o cuatro veces.

SCORE [   ]

B. Rosario's family is getting ready for a trip. Complete her statements and questions to her brother Suso about where everyone went while getting ready. Use the correct preterite forms of **ir**. (9 points)

11.   Mamá y yo _____ al almacén para comprar ropa.

12.   Luego, yo _____ a casa para hacer la maleta.

13.   Geraldo _____ al centro comercial para buscar una maleta nueva.

14.   Suso, tú ya _____ al banco, ¿verdad?

15.   Después, tú y papá _____ a la librería para comprar un mapa, ¿no?

16.   Y más tarde papá y Geraldo _____ al correo para comprar estampillas.

SCORE [   ]

Quiz 12-3A

C. Complete the sentences about what different people did in the countries they visited last summer. Use the correct preterite form of the verbs in parentheses and the Spanish names for the countries. (11 points)

— Yo 17. _____ (caminar) por los bosques en 18. _____ .
(Germany)

— Mis tíos 19. _____ (visitar) muchos museos en 20. _____ .
(England)

— Rubén y Teresa 21. _____ (sacar) muchas fotos de las pirámides en

22. _____ .
(Egypt)

— Martina, tú 23. _____ (escalar) montañas y 24. _____

(estudiar) italiano en 25. _____ , ¿verdad?
(Italy)

— Alicia 26. _____ (explorar) Pekín, la capital de 27. _____ .
(China)

SCORE [_____]

TOTAL SCORE [____ /35]

Spanish 1 ¡Ven conmigo!, Chapter 12

12 Las vacaciones ideales

■ TERCER PASO

Maximum Score: 35

I. Listening

A. Listen as Marta and Julio talk about what she and her family did on their trip around the world. First put the events of their trip in the order they happened. Then choose the best answer for the three questions that follow. (14 points)

a.

b.

c.

d.

1. _____   2. _____   3. _____   4. _____

_____ 5. When Marta went mountain climbing, she was in _____.
    a. Germany
    b. China

_____ 6. Marta _____ tired of traveling.
    a. is
    b. is not

_____ 7. Marta _____ like to visit several Spanish-speaking countries.
    a. would
    b. would not

SCORE [ ]

II. Reading

B. Read the sentences that María Elena wrote about a trip she took. Then arrange the sentences in the correct order. (9 points)

    a. En Puerto Rico compré regalos para toda mi familia.
    b. Regresé a Nueva York muy cansada y muy feliz.
    c. Hice la maleta y fui al aeropuerto, donde compré un boleto de ida y vuelta *(round-trip)*.
    d. También nadé y fui de vela.
    e. Mi amiga Rosa me invitó a visitarla en Puerto Rico.
    f. Le escribí a ella aceptando *(accepting)* la invitación.

8. _____   9. _____   10. _____   11. _____   12. _____   13. _____

SCORE [ ]

Quiz 12-3B

III. Writing

C. Your pen pal recently went on a vacation and you want to know about his trip. Write seven questions in Spanish asking him where he went and what he did. Be sure to ask him what activities or sports he did. (12 points)

14. _____

_____

15. _____

_____

16. _____

_____

17. _____

_____

18. _____

_____

19. _____

_____

SCORE ☐

TOTAL SCORE ☐ /35

CUMULATIVE SCORE FOR QUIZZES 1–3 ☐ /100

12 Las vacaciones ideales

Chapter 12 Test

I. Listening

Maximum Score: 30 points

A. You overhear people talking about plans. Decide if what you hear refers to **a) a future plan**, **b) what was done**, or **c) what is done every day**. (20 points)

1. _____
2. _____
3. _____
4. _____
5. _____

6. _____
7. _____
8. _____
9. _____
10. _____

SCORE [____]

B. Listen as people say what they feel like doing or what they would like to do. Write the letter of the picture that corresponds. One picture will not be used. (10 points)

a.   b.   c.   d.   e.   f.

11. _____   12. _____   13. _____   14. _____   15. _____   SCORE [____]

II. Reading

Maximum Score: 30 points

C. Read the following letter that Elena wrote to her new pen pal. Then choose the correct letter to complete each statement. (10 points)

Querido Raúl,

16. ¡Hola! Permíteme presentarme. _____ Elena.
   a. Estoy   **b.** Soy   **c.** Eres

17. _____ de Puerto Rico y mi familia todavía vive allí.
   a. Estoy   **b.** Es   **c.** Soy

18. Este año estoy viviendo en Nueva York con mis tíos. Asisto a una escuela que _____ muy lejos de nuestra casa.
    a. está **b.** es **c.** eres

19. Mis padres _____ en Nueva York ahora visitándome. Pasamos mucho tiempo comprando regalos para mis hermanos.
    a. están **b.** fueron **c.** son

20. Y tú, ¿cómo _____? ¿Qué te gusta hacer?
    a. es **b.** eres **c.** está

Escríbeme pronto,
Elena

SCORE

D. Look at the list of programs about outdoor activities in various countries on the TV schedule below. Then read what the following people like to do. Indicate which program each person would most likely enjoy watching by writing the correct letter. (10 points)

TV 2		domingo
	Presentación	
9:15	**a.** Francia	bajar el río en canoa
9:45	**b.** Inglaterra	dar una caminata
10:15	**c.** Alemania	escalar montañas
10:45	**d.** China	ir de vela
11:15	**e.** Estados Unidos	saltar en paracaídas

_____ 21. Alicia
Tengo dos pasatiempos. Me encanta viajar, y me gusta muchísimo saltar de avión. Mi sueño es ver este país desde el aire.

_____ 22. Pablo
Todos los días salgo para caminar por el bosque. Me gustaría acampar en los bosques de Inglaterra.

_____ 23. Éster
Me gustaría viajar a Europa algún día. Quiero ver los Alpes. Me encantan las montañas.

_____ 24. David
Me encanta nadar y hacer excursiones por el río.

_____ 25. Raquel
Me gusta nadar e ir en barco, especialmente cuando hace mucho viento.

SCORE

Chapter 12 Test

E. Read the letter that José wrote to his friend Manuel while on vacation. Then answer **a) cierto** or **b) falso** to the following statements. (10 points)

13 de julio

Querido Manuel,

¡España es fabuloso! Todo es muy interesante y divertido. Mamá, Papá, Ana y yo llegamos el miércoles por la tarde y fuimos al hotel. El hotel es un viejo castillo° histórico que es muy bonito y cómodo. Tiene cuartos grandísimos y la gente es muy simpática. Aquí podemos hacer de todo. Ayer fui de vela y Ana se quedó en la playa y tomó el sol. Papá saltó en paracaídas y Mamá fue a hacer turismo con otras personas del hotel. Hoy vamos a comprar boletos y vamos a ver un drama en el Teatro Colón. Más tarde, pensamos ir de compras para comprar recuerdos para todos. A nosotros nos encanta este lugar. Nos gustaría regresar el próximo año. Bueno, Manuel, ahora tengo que terminar esta carta porque es la hora de salir. Nos vemos pronto.

Tu amigo,
José

_____ 26. José does not like the hotel.

castillo *castle*

_____ 27. José went hiking yesterday.

_____ 28. Ana went to the beach to sunbathe.

_____ 29. The family saw a play at a theater yesterday.

_____ 30. José's family would like to return to Spain.

SCORE [   ]

III. Culture

Maximum Score: 10 points

F. Based on the information in your textbook, answer **a) cierto** or **b) falso** to the following statements. (4 points)

_____ 31. Many old castles in Spain have been turned into **paradores**.

_____ 32. The rooms in **paradores** are usually reasonably priced.

SCORE [   ]

Chapter 12 Test

G. Based on the information in your textbook, give two examples of what teenagers in Spanish-speaking countries do while on vacation. (6 points)

33. _____

34. _____

SCORE [   ]

IV. Writing

Maximum Score: 30 points

H. Based on the pictures, write a sentence in Spanish saying what people did as indicated by the pictures. Use the cues to begin your sentences. (8 points)

yo

nosotros

tú

ellos

35. Yo _____ en Chile.

36. Nosotros _____ ayer.

37. Tú _____ en el Brasil.

38. Ellos _____ en la selva.

SCORE [   ]

I. Write a conversation based on the following situation. Marisa can't decide what to do on her vacation. Juan is trying to help her decide by asking her questions about what she would like to do and where she would like to go. (12 points)

39. JUAN _____

_____

_____

MARISA _____

_____

_____

JUAN _____

_____

_____

MARISA _____

_____

JUAN _____

_____

_____

MARISA _____

_____

_____

SCORE [   ]

Chapter 12 Test

J. You have just received a letter from a friend asking about your vacation. Answer her, telling where you went, what you did, and what you liked about it. Give the order in which you did things (what you did first, what you did next, etc.). Write at least five sentences. (10 points)

40. _____

_____

_____

_____

_____

_____

_____

_____

_____

_____

_____

_____

_____

_____

_____

_____

_____

SCORE [   ]

TOTAL SCORE [   ] /100

Spanish 1 ¡Ven conmigo!, Chapter 12

Nombre _____ Clase _____ Fecha _____

CAPÍTULO 12 Chapter Test Score Sheet

Circle the letter that matches the most appropriate response.

I. Listening
Maximum Score: 30 points

A. (20 points)

1. a b c
2. a b c
3. a b c
4. a b c
5. a b c

6. a b c
7. a b c
8. a b c
9. a b c
10. a b c

SCORE [   ]

B. (10 points)

11. a b c d e
12. a b c d e
13. a b c d e
14. a b c d e
15. a b c d e

SCORE [   ]

II. Reading
Maximum Score: 30 points

C. (10 points)

16. a b c
17. a b c
18. a b c
19. a b c
20. a b c

SCORE [   ]

D. (10 points)

21. a b c d e
22. a b c d e
23. a b c d e
24. a b c d e
25. a b c d e

SCORE [   ]

E. (10 points)

26. a b
27. a b
28. a b
29. a b
30. a b

SCORE [   ]

III. Culture
Maximum Score: 10 points

F. (4 points)

31. a b
32. a b

SCORE [   ]

G. (6 points)

33. _____

34. _____

SCORE [   ]

Spanish 1 ¡Ven conmigo!, Chapter 12

Testing Program **319**

CAPÍTULO 12

IV. Writing

Maximum Score: 30 points

H. (8 points)

35. _____

36. _____

37. _____

38. _____

SCORE [ ]

I. (12 points)

39. JUAN _____

_____

MARISA _____

_____

JUAN _____

_____

MARISA _____

_____

JUAN _____

_____

MARISA _____

_____

SCORE [ ]

J. (10 points)

40. _____

_____

_____

_____

_____

_____

_____

_____

_____

_____

SCORE [ ]

TOTAL SCORE [ ] /100

Spanish 1 ¡Ven conmigo!, Chapter 12

Quiz 12-1B Capítulo 12 Primer paso

I. Listening

A. 1. Me gusta la playa y también el mar. En la playa del hotel, puedo tomar el sol. Cuando voy a la playa necesito llevar el bloqueador y los lentes del sol.

2. Pienso ir a hablar con la profesora Méndez. Tengo un examen de historia mañana y no estoy preparado. Creo que debo estudiar más.

3. Me encanta visitar las ciudades grandes. En esta ciudad puedo ver los museos, ir al teatro y asistir a un concierto de música clásica.

4. No me siento muy bien. Me duelen los dedos y las manos porque practiqué el piano demasiado anoche.

5. Pienso comprar unos dulces para el cumpleaños de mi abuela. A mí me encantan los dulces pero cuando como demasiados, me duele el estómago. Sin embargo, sé que a ella le van a encantar.

6. Mi prima va a cumplir los quince años y necesito un regalo especial. Pienso regalarle un collar de oro o unos aretes de plata. A ella le encantan las joyas.

Quiz 12-2B Capítulo 12 Segundo paso

I. Listening

A. 1. Esta foto es mi favorita. A mi hermano le gusta acampar, pero tuvo muchos problemas con la tienda de camping.

2. En esta foto, mi hermana está saltando en paracaídas. Es muy peligroso, ¿sabes?

3. —¿Qué pasa en ésta? ¿Quiénes están tomando refrescos?
—Ellos son mis amigos Roberto y Lorenzo.

4. En esta foto mi padre está escalando montañas en Colorado.

5. Y la última. Aquí está mi amigo Juan. Le encanta tomar el sol.

Quiz 12-3B Capítulo 12 Tercer paso

I. Listening

A. JULIO ¿Adónde viajaron tú y tu familia el año pasado?

MARTA Uy, fuimos a muchos países... ¡viajamos por todo el mundo!

JULIO Bueno, pero... ¿adónde fueron primero?

MARTA Primero a China. Allí caminamos y bajamos el río en canoa. ¡Fue toda una aventura!

JULIO ¿Y después?

MARTA Después fuimos a Egipto.

JULIO Y, ¿qué hiciste cuando fuiste allí?

MARTA Yo fui a visitar las pirámides, pero mi hermano Gabriel saltó en paracaídas. ¿Te imaginas?

JULIO ¡Fantástico! Visitaste Francia también, ¿verdad?

MARTA Sí, luego fuimos a Francia, donde yo fui a la playa y tomé el sol.

JULIO ¿Y por último?

MARTA Mi papá regresó a los Estados Unidos, pero yo fui a Alemania con mi mamá y con Gabriel. Allí escalé montañas con un grupo de viajeros de Italia... Y tú, Julio, ¿qué hiciste después de clases el año pasado?

JULIO ¿Yo? ¡Nada! Trabajé todos los días y no fui a ningún lugar. Pero ahora tengo vacaciones.

MARTA Pues, debes hacer las maletas. ¡Tengo ganas de viajar otra vez! Quiero visitar Ecuador, Paraguay, Santo Domingo, España... (fade)

CAPÍTULO 12

ANSWERS Quiz 12-1A

A. (15 points: 1.5 points per item)
1. empiezan
2. prefiero/puedo
3. tiene
4. tienen
5. almuerzo
6. almorzamos
7. preferimos/podemos
8. vienen
9. pueden
10. tenemos

B. (10 points: 1 point per item)
11. una bufanda
12. unos esquís
13. una cámara
14. una chaqueta
15. un boleto
16. unos lentes de sol
17. una maleta
18. unas chancletas
19. un traje de baño
20. una toalla

C. (5 points: 1 point per item)
21. vamos a
22. quiero
23. tengo que
24. necesitas
25. vas a

ANSWERS Quiz 12-1B

I. Listening

A. (12 points: 2 points per item)
1. b
2. c
3. e
4. d
5. f
6. a

II. Reading

B. (10 points: 2 points per item)
7. S
8. B
9. C
10. B
11. S

III. Writing

C. (8 points: 2 points per item)
Answers will vary. Possible answers:
12. Yuka va a esquiar.
13. Pablo quiere ir a Nueva York.
14. Leonardo espera asistir a la universidad.
15. María piensa mirar la televisión.

ANSWERS Quiz 12-2A

A. (9 points: 1.5 points per item)
Answers may vary. Possible answers:
1. Pilar está haciendo turismo/sacando fotos.
2. Luis y Curro están acampando.
3. Mi familia y yo estamos dando una caminata/explorando.
4. Tú y Maricarmen están bajando el río en canoa.
5. Mis primos están tomando el sol.
6. Estoy saltando en paracaídas.

B. (10 points: 1 point per item)
7. te
8. gustaría
9. me
10. gustaría
11. nos
12. gustaría
13. les
14. gustaría
15. le
16. gustaría

C. (16 points: 2 points per item)
17. eres
18. Soy
19. estoy
20. estoy
21. estás
22. estamos
23. es
24. son

ANSWERS Quiz 12-2B

I. Listening

A. (10 points: 2 points per item)
1. a
2. e
3. c
4. b
5. d

II. Reading

B. (10 points: 2 points per item)
6. b
7. a
8. b
9. b
10. a

III. Writing

C. (10 points: 2 points per item)
Answers may vary. Possible answers:
11. Estoy en la Península de Yucatán.
12. Estoy muy feliz.
13. Las playas son muy bonitas y el hotel es muy grande.
14. Ahora estoy tomando el sol y bebiendo un refresco.
15. Más tarde, nos gustaría saltar en paracaídas en la playa.

IV. Culture

D. (5 points: 2.5 points per item)
16. b
17. a

Answers to Quizzes 12-3A, 12-3B

CAPITULO 12

ANSWERS Quiz 12-3A

A. (15 points: 1.5 points per item)
1. Viajaste
2. pasé
3. Trabajé
4. jugué
5. jugó
6. tomó
7. estudió
8. hablamos
9. Nadaron
10. pescamos

B. (9 points: 1.5 points per item)
11. fuimos
12. fui
13. fue
14. fuiste
15. fueron
16. fueron

C. (11 points: 1 point per item)
17. caminé
18. Alemania
19. visitaron
20. Inglaterra
21. sacaron
22. Egipto
23. escalaste
24. estudiaste
25. Italia
26. exploró
27. China

ANSWERS Quiz 12-3B

I. Listening

A. (14 points: 2 points per item)
1. b
2. a
3. d
4. c
5. a
6. b
7. a

II. Reading

B. (9 points: 1.5 points per item)
8. e
9. f
10. c
11. a
12. d
13. b

III. Writing

C. (12 points: 2 points per item)
Answers will vary. Possible answers:
14. ¿Adónde fuiste de vacaciones?
15. ¿Qué hiciste allí?
16. ¿Nadaste en el océano?
17. ¿Bajaste el río en canoa?
18. ¿Escalaste montañas?
19. ¿Visitaste a tus primos?

I. Listening

A. 1. Algún día pienso viajar a Alemania.
   2. Tú y tu familia fueron a la China el verano pasado.
   3. Antonio jugó al jai alai en la Florida.
   4. Mi hermana quiere escalar montañas en enero.
   5. Salgo con mis amigos todas las tardes.
   6. Durante las últimas vacaciones no fui a ningún lugar.
   7. En Egipto visité las pirámides.
   8. Vas a hacer la maleta a las dos, ¿verdad?
   9. Todos los días a la una, miro mi programa favorito.
  10. ¿Qué haces todos los días después de clases?

B. 11. Tengo ganas de visitar a mi abuelo.
  12. Me gustaría explorar la selva.
  13. Me gustaría ir a Inglaterra para visitar Londres.
  14. Prefiero ir de vela con mis amigos cuando hace calor.
  15. A mí me gustaría llevar mi toalla y pasar el día tomando el sol.

I. Listening Maximum Score: 30 points

A. (20 points: 2 points per item)

1. a	6. b
2. b	7. b
3. b	8. a
4. a	9. c
5. c	10. c

B. (10 points: 2 points per item)

11. b
12. d
13. c
14. e
15. a

II. Reading Maximum Score: 30 points

C. (10 points: 2 points per item)

16. Soy
17. Soy
18. está
19. están
20. eres

D. (10 points: 2 points per item)

21. e
22. b
23. c
24. a
25. d

E. (10 points: 2 points per item)

26. b
27. b
28. a
29. b
30. a

III. Culture Maximum Score: 10 points

F. (4 points: 2 points per item)

31. a
32. a

G. (6 points: 3 points per item)
Answers will vary. Possible answers:

33. go to the beach
34. spend time with family and friends

IV. Writing Maximum Score: 30 points

H. (8 points: 2 points per item)
Answers will vary. Possible answers:

35. Yo escalé una montaña en Chile.
36. Nosotros fuimos de vela ayer.
37. Tú bajaste el río en canoa en el Brasil.
38. Ellos exploraron en la selva.

I. (12 points)

39. Answers will vary. Possible answers:
    J: ¿Qué te gustaría hacer este verano?
    M: No sé.
    J: Pues, ¿te gustan las montañas?
    M: Sí, muchísimo.
    J: Hay montañas in Colorado. ¿Te gustaría ir a Colorado?
    M: Sí, tengo ganas de ir a Colorado.

J. (10 points)

40. Answers will vary. Possible answers.
    Primero fui a España. Cené en muchos restaurantes. Me gustó mucho la comida.
    Después fui a Inglaterra. Caminé todo el tiempo. Me gustó hacer turismo en Londres.
    Luego regresé a Los Ángeles.

Final Exam Capítulos 7–12

I. Listening

Maximum Score: 30 points

A. Listen as Jorge and Marta talk about their vacation plans. Then based on their conversation, choose the best answer to each question. (5 points)

_____ 1. ¿Qué piensa hacer Marta?
    a. viajar a Puerto Rico
    b. viajar a América del Sur

_____ 2. ¿Adónde va a ir Jorge?
    a. a ningún lugar
    b. a Rio de Janeiro

_____ 3. ¿Qué piensa comprar Marta?
    a. una chaqueta y botas de cuero
    b. unos esquís y una tienda de camping

_____ 4. ¿Qué les gustaría hacer a los padres de Marta?
    a. tomar el sol
    b. hacer turismo

_____ 5. ¿Qué le gustaría hacer a la hermana de Marta?
    a. bajar el río en canoa
    b. escalar montañas

SCORE [____]

B. Listen to the following statements and decide if they are **a) logical** or **b) illogical**. (10 points)

_____ 6.   _____ 11.

_____ 7.   _____ 12.

_____ 8.   _____ 13.

_____ 9.   _____ 14.

_____ 10.   _____ 15.

SCORE [____]

C. Listen to the following morning announcements at the Centro Unión high school. Decide if the following events **a) have already taken place** or **b) are going to happen**. (10 points)

_____ 16.   _____ 21.

_____ 17.   _____ 22.

_____ 18.   _____ 23.

_____ 19.   _____ 24.

_____ 20.   _____ 25.

SCORE [____]

FINAL EXAM

Nombre _____ Clase _____ Fecha _____

D. Today is a very busy day in the downtown commercial area of the city. Listen to the following conversations and decide in which of the stores they are taking place. (5 points)

_____ 26.

_____ 27.

_____ 28.

_____ 29.

_____ 30.

a. Pastelería La Concha
b. Joyería La Perla
c. Florería Rosas Rojas
d. Dulcería El Cacahuate
e. Zapatería El Taconcito

SCORE ☐

II. Reading

Maximum Score: 20 points

A. Read the following questions and select the best answer to each one. (5 points)

_____ 31. ¿Qué te parece si invitamos a Juan a la fiesta?

_____ 32. ¿Crees que hay bastante comida?

_____ 33. ¿Crees que mandamos bastantes invitaciones?

_____ 34. ¿Qué te parece si le pedimos a Jorge sus discos compactos?

_____ 35. ¿Daniel va a traer los refrescos?

a. Perfecto. Él tiene muy buena música.
b. Creo que sí porque él fue al supermercado por la mañana.
c. Creo que sí porque Renato y Patricia prepararon mucho arroz con pollo.
d. ¡Buena idea! Él toca muy bien la guitarra.
e. ¡Claro que sí! Todos los amigos de la escuela recibieron una.

SCORE ☐

B. Find the best answer to each of the following questions. (5 points)

_____ 36. ¿Me haces el favor de llamar a Manuel?

_____ 37. ¿Me ayudas a limpiar mi cuarto?

_____ 38. ¿Me traes una silla?

_____ 39. ¿Me ayudas con los regalos?

_____ 40. ¿Me ayudas a decorar la sala?

a. ¡Con mucho gusto! Y luego tú me ayudas a limpiar el mío.
b. Sí, hombre. ¿Tienes los globos?
c. Claro que sí. ¿Cuál es su número de teléfono?
d. Lo siento, pero no puedo. Me duele mucho la espalda.
e. ¿Dónde los ponemos, en la sala o en el patio?

SCORE ☐

Spanish 1 ¡Ven conmigo!, Final Exam

Nombre _____ Clase _____ Fecha _____

C. Read these tips about controlling stress. Then look at the following statements about several students and decide if each one is following the article's advice. Using only the information in the article, choose **a) if the student seems to be doing a good job of managing stress** or **b) if the student's habits could be improved.** (5 points)

7 Claves *para manejar el* **ESTRÉS**

1 Comer por lo menos una comida balanceada al día. La nutrición es esencial para una buena salud y proporciona defensas contra el estrés.

2 Dormir por lo menos 8 horas cada noche. Un sueño apropiado puede añadir años de vida. Trate de acostarse y levantarse a la misma hora.

3 Hacer ejercicio, por lo menos 3 veces por semana. Busque una actividad divertida, como montar en bicicleta, caminar o nadar.

4 No debe tomar demasiada cafeína. Puede producir irritabilidad, dolor de cabeza, ansiedad y depresión.

5 Salir y cultivar sus amistades. Tener amigos ayuda a mantener en alto la auto-estima.

6 Organizar su tiempo. Planee su uso y empléelo.

7 Conservar una actitud positiva: las personas optimistas tienen menos problemas mentales y físicos.

Adaptation from "17 Claves para manejar el Estrés" (Retitled: "7 Claves para manejar el Estrés") from *Bienestar*, no. 9. Copyright © by *Colsanitas*. Reprinted by permission of the publisher.

_____ 41. Ana Luisa hace ejercicio los fines de semana.

_____ 42. Javier tiene muchos amigos, pero Fabio es un amigo muy especial que lo ayuda mucho con sus problemas.

_____ 43. ¡Qué chico tan organizado es Pepe! Siempre sabe exactamente lo que va a hacer y cuándo lo va a hacer.

_____ 44. Rosana es una amiga muy buena, pero me parece que siempre piensa en cosas negativas.

_____ 45. Nora nunca desayuna pero compra un almuerzo balanceado todos los días.

SCORE [   ]

D. Carlos has had a terrible day. Read the following entry in his diary and decide if the statements below are **a) true** or **b) false**. (5 points)

jueves 2 de abril

Querido diario:

Hoy fue un día horrible. Le hice cuatro invitaciones a Elisa y ella me contestó que no a todas. Primero, la invité a ir al partido de fútbol conmigo mañana, y ella respondió: "¡Qué lástima! Ya tengo planes. Tal vez otro día". Luego, la invité al cine el sábado y me contestó: "Lo siento, pero tengo una cita con Pablo". Después la invité a comer pizza esta tarde y me dijo: "Me gustaría, pero no puedo. Estoy cansada y tengo sueño". Luego, la invité a ir al museo el domingo, y ella me dijo: "Lo siento, pero tengo que estudiar álgebra". Finalmente, ella me invitó a jugar al voleibol la próxima semana, ¡pero no puedo! Voy a estar en San Antonio para jugar en el campeonato de béisbol.

_____ **46.** Carlos invitó a Elisa a comer pizza hoy.

_____ **47.** Elisa tiene una cita con Pablo el sábado.

_____ **48.** Elisa ya tiene planes para mañana.

_____ **49.** Elisa no quiere ir al museo porque tiene que estudiar álgebra.

_____ **50.** Finalmente Carlos y Elisa deciden ir a un partido de béisbol.

SCORE [   ]

III. Culture

Maximum Score: 15 points

A. Read the following descriptions and indicate whether the person is more likely to be from a) **the United States** or b) **a Spanish-speaking country**. (5 points)

_____ 51. Gloria buys everything in a large supermarket.

_____ 52. Andrea's family eats a very light supper.

_____ 53. Carolina uses **pesos** when shopping.

_____ 54. Daniel drives his car everywhere.

_____ 55. David thinks soccer is more important than football.

SCORE [   ]

B. Are the following statements a) **true** or b) **false**? (5 points)

_____ 56. Students in Latin American schools are provided with all books and supplies.

_____ 57. People in Spanish-speaking countries often celebrate their saint's day in addition to their birthday.

_____ 58. Some monetary units in Latin America are named after Spanish explorers.

_____ 59. Many girls in Spanish-speaking countries have a big celebration on their fifteenth birthday.

_____ 60. Baseball is the national sport in Spain and in Mexico.

SCORE [   ]

C. Choose the most appropriate answer to complete each statement below. (5 points)

_____ 61. Families in Spanish-speaking countries often do not have cars because _____.
   a. public transportation is convenient and inexpensive
   b. they are usually more expensive
   c. a and b

_____ 62. Religious and public celebrations in Spanish-speaking countries are often _____.
   a. closely related
   b. very different
   c. neither of the above

_____ 63. Many Spanish-speaking baseball players in the U.S. come from _____.
   a. Spain
   b. Chile
   c. Puerto Rico

_____ 64. Spain's **paradores**, or inns, are usually _____.
   a. new hotels
   b. old castles and convents
   c. new palaces

_____ 65. In Venezuela, you pay your bills with _____.
   a. **pesos**
   b. **bolívares**
   c. **colones**

SCORE [   ]

FINAL EXAM

IV. Writing

Maximum Score: 35 points

A. Imagine that you're studying for a year in a Spanish-speaking country. How would you ask for the following information? Write a complete question for each topic. (10 points)

How would you . . . ?

66. ask your computer science teacher what his name is

_____

67. ask a new friend where she or he is from

_____

68. ask a group of schoolmates what they're going to do after class today

_____

69. ask someone on campus to tell you where the library is

_____

70. politely ask a bystander what time it is

_____

SCORE ☐

B. The family you're staying with while studying in a Spanish-speaking country often asks you questions. Write a complete sentence to answer each question below. (10 points)

71. ¿Qué regalos piensas comprar para tu familia?

_____

_____

72. ¿Qué te gusta tomar para el almuerzo?

_____

_____

73. ¿Qué te gustaría hacer este fin de semana?

_____

_____

FINAL EXAM

74. ¿Adónde fuiste ayer? Te llamé a las cuatro.

_____

_____

75. ¿Qué te gustaría hacer para las vacaciones este año? ¿Por qué?

_____

_____

SCORE [   ]

C. Now that you've been living in Pueblo Nuevo for a while, you know your way around better than most foreigners. Imagine that you're standing at the spot marked with an X. Help the newer visitors by completing the directions to the places they're looking for. (5 points)

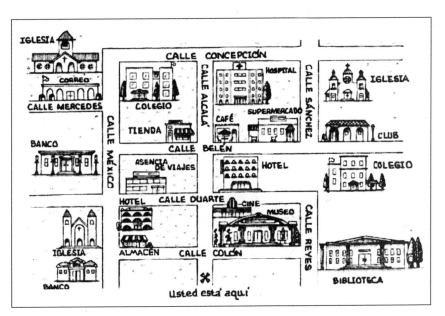

76. ¿La tienda? No, no queda lejos. Está a dos _____ de aquí.

77. Sí, señorita, el correo _____ en la calle Mercedes.

78. Mire, señor, la biblioteca está muy _____ de aquí.

79. Sí, el supermercado está _____ del café.

80. ¿El colegio? Pues, está un poco _____ de aquí, en la Calle Concepción.

SCORE [   ]

Nombre _____ Clase _____ Fecha _____

D. Write a paragraph in Spanish describing your dream vacation. Make sure that you include the following elements: where you want to go and why, who you want to go with, and several things you plan to do there. Be creative! (10 points)

81. _____

_____

_____

_____

_____

_____

_____

SCORE [   ]

TOTAL SCORE [   ] /100

Spanish 1 ¡Ven conmigo!, Final Exam

Nombre _____ Clase _____ Fecha _____

Circle the letter that matches the most appropriate response.

I. Listening
Maximum Score: 30 points

A. (5 points)   **B.** (10 points)   **C.** (10 points)   **D.** (5 points)

1. a b   6. a b   16. a b   26. a b c d e
2. a b   7. a b   17. a b   27. a b c d e
3. a b   8. a b   18. a b   28. a b c d e
4. a b   9. a b   19. a b   29. a b c d e
5. a b   10. a b   20. a b   30. a b c d e
               11. a b   21. a b
               12. a b   22. a b
               13. a b   23. a b
               14. a b   24. a b
               15. a b   25. a b

SCORE [   ]   SCORE [   ]   SCORE [   ]   SCORE [   ]

II. Reading
Maximum Score: 20 points

A. (5 points)   **B.** (5 points)   **C.** (5 points)   **D.** (5 points)

31. a b c d e   36. a b c d e   41. a b   46. a b
32. a b c d e   37. a b c d e   42. a b   47. a b
33. a b c d e   38. a b c d e   43. a b   48. a b
34. a b c d e   39. a b c d e   44. a b   49. a b
35. a b c d e   40. a b c d e   45. a b   50. a b

SCORE [   ]   SCORE [   ]   SCORE [   ]   SCORE [   ]

FINAL EXAM

Spanish 1 ¡Ven conmigo!, Final Exam

III. Culture

Maximum Score: 15 points

A. (5 points)

51. a b

52. a b

53. a b

54. a b

55. a b

SCORE _____

B. (5 points)

56. a b

57. a b

58. a b

59. a b

60. a b

SCORE _____

C. (5 points)

61. a b c

62. a b c

63. a b c

64. a b c

65. a b c

SCORE _____

IV. Writing

Maximum Score: 35 points

A. (10 points)

66. _____

67. _____

68. _____

69. _____

70. _____

SCORE _____

B. (10 points)

71. _____

72. _____

73. _____

74. _____

75. _____

SCORE _____

FINAL EXAM

Spanish 1 ¡Ven conmigo!, Final Exam

C. (5 points)

76. _____

77. _____

78. _____

79. _____

80. _____

SCORE ☐

D. (10 points)

81. _____

_____

_____

_____

_____

_____

_____

_____

SCORE ☐

TOTAL SCORE ☐ /100

FINAL EXAM

Listening Scripts for Final Exam

I. Listening

A.

JORGE	Hola, Marta. ¿Cómo estás?
MARTA	Estupendo, ¿y tú?
JORGE	Muy bien. Oye, ¿qué piensas hacer durante las vacaciones de verano?
MARTA	Pienso viajar a América del Sur con mi familia. Nos gustaría visitar Brasil, Argentina y Chile. ¿Y tú? ¿Qué vas a hacer este verano?
JORGE	Me gustaría viajar a Puerto Rico para visitar a mis abuelos, pero no puedo. Tengo que trabajar mucho. Voy a trabajar en el Almacén García. Oye, tú vas a necesitar ropa para tu viaje, ¿no?
MARTA	Sí, en América del Sur es invierno ahora y hace mucho frío en Chile y Argentina. Pienso comprar una chaqueta nueva y unas botas de cuero.
JORGE	Maravilloso. Hay muchas gangas en el Almacén García y yo te puedo ayudar a encontrar cosas baratas. Pero en Brasil no va hacer mucho frío, ¿verdad?
MARTA	No. Además, pienso ir a la playa a tomar el sol y al Amazonas a bajar el río en canoa. A mis padres les gustaría hacer turismo en Rio de Janeiro y a mi hermana le gustaría escalar montañas. Por eso vamos a los Andes en Chile.
JORGE	Entonces, ¿también vas a comprar ropa para la playa?
MARTA	¡Claro! Un traje de baño nuevo, unas sandalias y unos lentes de sol.
JORGE	Muy bien, Marta. ¿Te gustaría ir al Almacén García con toda tu familia?
MARTA	Por supuesto, Jorge. Nos encantan las gangas. Chao.
JORGE	Hasta pronto.

B.

6. Tengo que lavarme los dientes antes de comer.
7. ¿Me puede traer una decoración para el almuerzo?
8. ¡Tengo mucha sed! ¿Me puede traer el pan dulce?
9. Quisiera huevos con tocino para el desayuno.
10. ¡Uuy, qué frío! Me gustaría tomar un chocolate caliente.
11. Camarero, ¿me puede traer el menú?
12. ¿Te gustaría un flan para el postre?
13. ¡Tengo mucha hambre! Quisiera un café con leche, por favor.
14. Son dos galletas de propina.
15. ¡Los frijoles están deliciosos!

FINAL EXAM

C.

16. Ayer, los estudiantes del 301 celebraron los quince años de Socorro Martínez. El baile terminó hasta la media noche.

17. Los estudiantes de la clase de deportes van a ir a escalar la Montaña Encantada en el mes de julio.

18. La señorita María Moliner va a ir de vacaciones a España. A partir de mañana, no hay clases de español.

19. Ayer, los Ticos de San José no jugaron al béisbol porque estudiaron para el examen de geografía.

20. Mañana, María Ferreti va a dar una clase de literatura argentina en el Salón 201 a las tres de la tarde.

21. El mes pasado, todos los estudiantes del Centro Unión celebraron el aniversario de su escuela.

22. En mayo, la cafetería de la escuela no va a servir limonadas. Sólo jugos de naranja y de mango.

23. Mañana inician las clases especiales de álgebra del profesor Rodríguez.

24. La semana pasada, los estudiantes de fotografía fueron a la fiesta de aniversario del profesor Cuartoscuro.

25. El domingo pasado, los Huracanes de Barcelona ganaron el partido de fútbol contra los Bombones de Madrid.

D.

26. —Son cincuenta dólares.
    —¡Cincuenta dólares por un collar! ¡Es un robo!

27. —¡Estas flores rojas son preciosas! ¿Tú crees que le gusten a mamá?
    —¡Claro! Estas flores y una tarjeta la van a hacer feliz el Día de las Madres.

28. —¡Qué zapatos tan bonitos! ¡Te quedan muy bien!
    —Y además, ¡son muy baratos!

29. —Señorita, ¿me puede decir el precio de este pastel de fresa?
    —Lo siento, pero ese pastel es para una fiesta de cumpleaños. ¿Le gustaría un pastel de chocolate?

30. —¡Me encantan los chocolates!
    —Pero yo prefiero los dulces.

Answers to Final Exam

I. Listening Maximum Score: 30 points

A. (5 points: 1 point per item)
1. b
2. a
3. a
4. b
5. b

B. (10 points: 1 point per item)
6. b
7. b
8. b
9. a
10. a
11. a
12. a
13. b
14. b
15. a

C. (10 points: 1 point per item)
16. a
17. b
18. b
19. a
20. b
21. a
22. b
23. b
24. a
25. a

D. (5 points: 1 point per item)
26. b
27. c
28. e
29. a
30. d

II. Reading Maximum Score: 20 points

A. (5 points: 1 point per item)
31. d
32. c
33. e
34. a
35. b

B. (5 points: 1 point per item)
36. c
37. a
38. d
39. e
40. b

C. (5 points: 1 point per item)
41. b
42. a
43. a
44. b
45. a

D. (5 points: 1 point per item)
46. a
47. a
48. a
49. a
50. b

III. Culture Maximum Score: 15 points

A. (5 points: 1 point per item)
51. a
52. b
53. b
54. a
55. b

B. (5 points: 1 point per item)
56. b
57. a
58. a
59. a
60. b

C. (5 points: 1 point per item)
61. c
62. a
63. c
64. b
65. b

IV. Writing Maximum Score: 35 points

A. (10 points: 2 point per item)
66. ¿Cómo se llama usted?
67. ¿De dónde eres?
68. ¿Qué van a hacer ustedes hoy después de clase?
69. ¿Me puede(s) decir dónde queda la biblioteca?
70. ¿Qué hora es, por favor?

B. (10 points: 2 point per item) Answers will vary. Possible answers:
71. Pienso comprar una blusa para mi mamá y un cinturón de cuero para mi papá.
72. Me gusta tomar sopa con una ensalada o un sándwich para el almuerzo.
73. Tengo ganas de ver una película o cenar en un restaurante.
74. Fui a las canchas y jugué al tenis con Pedro.
75. Me gustaría ir a Colorado porque me encanta escalar montañas y acampar.

C. (5 points: 1 point per item)
76. cuadras
77. queda/está
78. cerca
79. al lado
80. lejos

D. (10 points) Answers will vary for item 81.

FINAL EXAM

To the Teacher

Speaking Tests

The primary goal of *¡Ven conmigo!* is to help students develop proficiency in Spanish. The speaking tests in the *Testing Program* have been designed to help assess students' proficiency in listening to and speaking Spanish. The speaking tests, which measure how well students use the language in contexts that approximate real-life situations, reflect the interview/role-play format of the Situation Cards in the *Activities for Communication*. You can choose whether to set up interviews with each student, role-play the short situations with individual students, or have pairs of students role-play the situations spontaneously as you observe.

Administering a speaking test requires approximately three to five minutes with each student or pair of students. You might administer a speaking test to one student or pair while the others are working on the reading and writing sections of a Chapter Test. Make sure that you and the student(s) are seated far enough from the others so that they will not be disturbed. Instruct the student(s) to speak in a soft but audible voice. If such an arrangement is not possible, meet with students at mutually agreed upon times outside class.

The Speaking Test Evaluation Form on page 342 will help you assess each student's performance. At the end of each test, take a moment to note your impression of the student's performance on the evaluation form. The following guidelines offer one possibility for assessing a student's global score, based on this evaluation.

18–20 pts: The student accomplishes the assigned task successfully, speaks clearly and accurately, and brings additional linguistic material to the basic situation, for example, using new functions or structures that beginning language learners seldom use spontaneously.

15–17 pts: The student accomplishes the assigned task successfully with a few errors. The student is able to communicate effectively in spite of these errors and offers meaningful responses.

12–14 pts: The student accomplishes the task with difficulty. He or she demonstrates minimum oral competence, hesitates frequently, and shows little creativity, offering only minimal, predictable responses.

9–11 pts: The student is unable to accomplish the task or fails to demonstrate acceptable mastery of functions, vocabulary, and grammatical concepts.

0–8 pts: Communication is almost non-existent. The student does not understand the aural cues and is unable to accomplish the task. Errors are so extreme that communication is impossible.

SPEAKING TESTS

Nombre _____ Clase _____ Fecha _____

 Speaking Test Evaluation Form

Chapter _____   ☐ Interview   ☐ Role-play   ☐ Other format

Targeted Function(s) _____
_____
_____

Context (Topic) _____

COMPREHENSION (ability to understand aural cues and respond appropriately)	(POOR)	1 2 3 4 (EXCELLENT)
COMPREHENSIBILITY (ability to communicate ideas and be understood)	(POOR)	1 2 3 4 (EXCELLENT)
ACCURACY (ability to use structures and vocabulary correctly)	(POOR)	1 2 3 4 (EXCELLENT)
FLUENCY (ability to communicate clearly and smoothly)	(POOR)	1 2 3 4 (EXCELLENT)
EFFORT (inclusion of details beyond the minimum predictable response)	(POOR)	1 2 3 4 (EXCELLENT)

TOTAL POINTS [   ]

NOTES:

_____
_____
_____
_____
_____
_____
_____

SPEAKING TESTS

Spanish 1 ¡Ven conmigo!, Speaking Test

¡Mucho gusto!

Speaking Test

Targeted Functions: saying hello and goodbye; introducing people and responding to an introduction; asking how someone is and saying how you are; asking and saying how old someone is; asking where someone is from and saying where you're from; talking about likes and dislikes

A. Interview
Have students respond to the following in Spanish.
1. Hola. ¿Cómo estás?
2. ¿Cómo te llamas?
3. ¿De dónde eres?
4. ¿Cuántos años tienes?
5. ¿Qué te gusta más, la música clásica o la música rock?

B. Role-play
Have pairs of students act out the following situation. You can also act it out with individual students.

You're a reporter for the school newspaper who is interviewing an exchange student from Spain. Greet the student, introduce yourself, and find out his or her name, age, and at least two likes and dislikes. End your conversation with an appropriate goodbye.

¡Organízate!

Speaking Test

Targeted Functions: talking about what you want and need; describing the contents of your room; talking about what you need and want to do

A. Interview
Have students respond to the following in Spanish.
1. ¿Qué necesitas para tus clases?
2. ¿Qué hay en tu cuarto?
3. ¿Qué hay en la clase de español?
4. ¿Necesitas ir al centro comercial?
5. ¿Qué quieres comprar para tus clases?

B. Role-play
Have pairs of students act out the following situation. You can also act it out with individual students.

You need to go shopping for school supplies. First make a list of all the items you need, then go shopping. Tell the salesperson the items and quantities you need. The salesperson will tell you if he or she has the items and how much each item costs.

SPEAKING TESTS

CAPÍTULO **3**

Nuevas clases, nuevos amigos

Speaking Test

Targeted Functions: talking about classes and sequencing events; telling time; telling at what time something happens; talking about being late or in a hurry; describing people and things; talking about things you like and explaining why

A. Interview
Have students respond to the following in Spanish.
1. ¿Qué hora es?
2. ¿A qué hora es la clase de español?
3. ¿Qué clases tienes hoy?
4. ¿Cómo son tus compañeros?
5. ¿Cuál es tu clase favorita? ¿Por qué?

B. Role-play
Have pairs of students act out the following situation. You can also act it out with individual students.

You have just received your new schedule for the semester. You meet your friend and discuss which classes you have and what times they meet. Tell why you like or don't like your schedule.

CAPÍTULO **4**

¿Qué haces esta tarde?

Speaking Test

Targeted Functions: talking about what you like to do; discussing what you and others do during free time; telling where people and things are; talking about where you and others go during free time

A. Interview
Have students respond to the following in Spanish.
1. ¿Qué te gusta hacer cuando estás en casa?
2. ¿Qué haces los sábados con tus amigos?
3. ¿Practicas deportes? ¿Cuáles?
4. ¿Dónde está el parque?
5. ¿Adónde vas con tu familia los fines de semana?

B. Role-play
Have pairs of students act out the following situation. You can also act it out with individual students.

You and a friend meet after school to talk about what to do this weekend. One of you will ask, **¿Qué haces este fin de semana?** You respond and ask your friend the same question. Talk about what things you like and don't like to do. Each of you should ask and answer at least five questions.

SPEAKING TESTS

Spanish 1 ¡Ven conmigo!, Speaking Tests

5 El ritmo de la vida

Speaking Test

Targeted Functions: discussing how often you do things; talking about what you and your friends like to do together; talking about what you do during a typical week; giving today's date; talking about the weather

A. Interview
Have your students respond to the following in Spanish.
1. ¿Qué tiempo hace hoy?
2. ¿Qué te gusta hacer cuando hace frío?
3. ¿Cuál es la fecha?
4. ¿Con qué frecuencia lees el periódico?
5. ¿Les gusta a ustedes asistir a conciertos de _____?
   (Choose current musical group)

B. Role-play
Have pairs of students act out the following situation. You can also act it out with individual students.

> You and a friend are trying to figure out what to do together. Your friend will ask, **¿Qué te gusta hacer cuando hace _____?** (He or she will give a weather expression.). You respond and ask your friend the same question. Discuss what activities you like and don't like to do in various weather conditions or seasons. Each of you should ask and answer at least five questions.

6 Entre familia

Speaking Test

Targeted Functions: describing a family; describing people; discussing things a family does together; discussing problems and giving advice

A. Interview
Have students respond to the following in Spanish.
1. ¿Cuántas personas hay en tu familia?
2. ¿Cómo son tus hermanos?
3. ¿De qué color es tu pelo? ¿De qué color son tus ojos?
4. ¿Qué hacen tú y tu familia juntos?
5. ¿Qué debes hacer para ayudar en casa?

B. Role-play
Have pairs of students act out the following situation. You can also act it out with individual students.

> You and a friend are talking about how overworked your parents are. You decide that it would be a good idea to do something to help out. One of you starts the conversation with **Pobrecitos de mis padres. Ellos trabajan demasiado.** The other person inquires what your parents do and then gives advice about how to help. Each of you suggests three things that other members of the family should do to help.

SPEAKING TESTS

CAPÍTULO

7 ¿Qué te gustaría hacer?

Speaking Test

Targeted Functions: talking on the telephone; extending and accepting invitations; making plans; talking about getting ready; turning down an invitation and explaining why

A. Interview
Have students respond to the following in Spanish.
1. ¿Te gustaría ir al circo conmigo?
2. ¿Qué piensas hacer el viernes?
3. ¿Tienes ganas de estudiar o ir al acuario?
4. ¿Cuándo prefieres ducharte?
5. ¿Ya tienes planes o quieres ir a una fiesta mañana?

B. Role-play
Have pairs of students act out the following situation. You can also act it out with individual students.

You call a friend to invite him or her to a surprise party you are throwing. Your friend will either accept the invitation and ask more about the party, or decline the invitation and give an appropriate, polite excuse and tell you what he or she is planning to do instead.

CAPÍTULO

8 ¡A comer!

Speaking Test

Targeted Functions: talking about meals and food; commenting on food; making polite requests; ordering dinner in a restaurant; asking for and paying the bill in a restaurant

A. Interview
Have students respond to the following in Spanish.
1. ¿Qué te gusta desayunar? ¿Y almorzar?
2. ¿Cómo está la comida de la cafetería?
3. ¿Cuál es más salado, las papitas o el pan dulce?
4. Cuando vas a un restaurante, ¿qué te gusta pedir? ¿Quién paga la cuenta?
5. ¿Cuál es tu plato favorito? ¿Por qué?

B. Role-play
Have pairs of students act out the following situation. You can also act it out with individual students.

You are at a restaurant. Order what you want to eat and drink, comment on the food, and pay the bill. Remember to be polite when speaking with the waiter or waitress, and don't forget to ask if the tip is included.

SPEAKING TESTS

Spanish 1 ¡Ven conmigo!, Speaking Tests

CAPÍTULO 9

¡Vamos de compras!

Targeted Functions: discussing gift suggestions; asking for and giving directions downtown; commenting on clothes; making comparisons; expressing preferences; asking about prices and paying for something

A. Interview
Have students respond to the following in Spanish.
1. ¿Qué piensas regalarle a tu mamá para su cumpleaños?
2. ¿Me puedes decir dónde está el centro comercial en esta ciudad?
3. ¿Prefieres llevar botas o zapatos de tenis? ¿Por qué?
4. ¿Qué ropa llevas cuando vas a una fiesta?
5. ¿Son más caras las camisetas o las blusas de seda? ¿Cuánto cuestan?

B. Role-play
Have pairs of students act out the following situation. You can also act it out with individual students.

You are in a store shopping for clothes to wear to a party this weekend. Tell the salesperson what you're looking for and find out if they have it in a certain material and color. Ask how much it costs and then tell the salesperson if you're going to buy it or not. If you decide to buy it, pay for it at the cashier.

CAPÍTULO 10

Celebraciones

Targeted Functions: talking about what you're doing right now; asking for and giving an opinion; asking for help and responding to requests; telling a friend what to do; talking about past events

A. Interview
Have students respond to the following in Spanish.
1. ¿Qué estás haciendo?
2. ¿Qué te parece si vamos al cine esta noche?
3. ¿Me puedes ayudar a decorar la clase?
4. ¿Cuál es tu día festivo favorito? ¿Por qué?
5. ¿Quién preparó la cena en tu casa anoche?

B. Role-play
Have pairs of students act out the following situation. You can also act it out with individual students.

You and a friend are planning a graduation party for another friend. Exchange ideas about what kind of gift to buy and decide who will do what to prepare for the party.

Para vivir bien

Targeted Functions: making suggestions and expressing feelings, talking about moods and physical condition; saying what you did; talking about where you went and when

A. Interview
Have students respond to the following in Spanish.
1. ¿Cómo estás? ¿Cómo te sientes hoy?
2. ¿Qué le pasa a tu mejor amigo(a)? ¿Está enfermo(a)?
3. ¿Por qué no vas al partido el viernes?
4. ¿Qué hiciste ayer?
5. ¿Adónde fueron tú y tu familia el fin de semana pasado?

B. Role-play
Have pairs of students act out the following situation. You can also act it out with individual students.

You are being interviewed for membership in a health club. The interviewer will ask you questions about your medical history and what you normally do to stay healthy. Answer the questions and make comments about how important you think the following things are ... ... gularly, etc. Mention what other things you sh... ...

CAPÍTULO

Las vacaciones ideales

Targeted Functions: talking about what you do and like to do every day; making future plans; discussing what you would like to do on vacation; saying where you went and what you did on vacation

A. Interview
Have students respond to the following in Spanish.
1. Por lo general, ¿qué haces durante la semana?
2. ¿Qué piensas hacer durante el verano?
3. ¿Te gustaría viajar a México? ¿Por qué sí o por qué no?
4. ¿Adónde fueron tú y tu familia durante las vacaciones?
5. ¿Qué hicieron? ¿Nadaron? ¿Montaron en bicicleta?

B. Role-play
Have pairs of students act out the following situation. You can also act it out with individual students.

You have just won a dream vacation and your friend wants to know all about it! He or she wants to know where you are going, what you plan to do there, and why you would like to go there. After you have answered your friend's questions, find out if he or she would like to do the same things.

SPEAKING TESTS

Spanish 1 ¡Ven conmigo!, Speaking Tests